Lottery

The Win that Tore a Family Apart

Rachel Halliwell

First published in Great Britain by
Virgin Publishing Ltd
Thames Wharf Studios
Rainville Road
London W6 9HT

ISBN 0 7535 0372 7

Typeset by TW Typesetting, Plymouth, Devon
Printed and bound by Mackays of Chatham PLC

Chapter One

KEN WHITE'S EYES DARTED between the piece of paper in his hand and the numbers dotted around the edges of the front page of the newspaper on his lap. The six numbers he had scribbled down as they flashed up on the TV screen matched those on one line of the ticket he was holding.

He felt nothing. No excitement, none of the euphoria he had expected would overwhelm him when he used to imagine what it would be like to win the lottery.

'Sheila, love,' he said calmly.

His wife sat with her legs tucked under her on the chair behind him. She leant forward and reached for another cigarette from the packet on the coffee table beside her. 'Mm?' she murmured as she lit it, her reading uninterrupted by the whole process.

'I've got six numbers.'

'Don't be daft,' said Sheila, turning the page as she took a deep drag on her cigarette.

'I'm bloody serious, woman,' said Ken, the tension now clear in his voice.

Sheila slammed her book shut and rose from the chair. 'Pass it here,' she said, snatching the ticket from his hand.

Ken pointed to one of the five lines on it and handed her his copy of the *Manchester Evening News*.

The paper had been the nearest thing to jot that night's winning numbers down on. He had sat glued to the TV since he got back from Asda with the week's shopping, leaving the carrier bags in a pile on the kitchen floor until the end of the rugby game. Ireland was playing the All Blacks in the World Cup. He had watched his national team, Wales, get beaten in the afternoon, but if Ireland won this game they could sneak through to the next round.

'Quick, switch on Teletext,' said Sheila, reaching over him to grab the remote. Ken got there first and found the right page.

They sat in silence as their eyes passed over the winning numbers. 'I've done it. I've bloody gone and done it,' said Ken slowly, enjoying each word as he said it. 'Didn't I tell you I'd do it one day – didn't I?'

'Yes, yes,' snapped Sheila. She sat staring intently at the screen in front of her, then turned her head sharply to face him. 'But how much?'

'How the bloody hell do I know how much?' He pulled himself up from his chair and walked to the door, heading for the kitchen.

'I was reading the other week that about a hundred people all thought they'd won millions but there were that many they didn't get much,' she jabbered.

'The news'll be on soon,' said Ken. 'They tell you how many have won. I'll put the shopping away and make a pot of tea while we wait.' He turned back towards her.

She wasn't listening. She had just got through on the phone to his sister Mavis in New Zealand. Ken shrugged, gently shaking his head, and carried on into the kitchen. There was no point in his even attempting to stop her from broadcasting their news to whomever she chose. Sheila was in full flow already and wouldn't listen to him now.

Inside, he shut the door behind him, blocking out Sheila's excited chatter. He held the kettle under the cold-water tap and stood, motionless, for a couple of minutes as he allowed himself to believe he really had won a fortune. He would give a million to each of his three sons, and Mavis, his beloved little sister, would get a pile too. And he would finally fulfil his lifelong dream of going to sea – something he had long since accepted would never happen. But instead of travelling the world's oceans as a sailor, he would do it in style in luxury cabins on the finest cruise ships.

Ken smiled to himself and turned on the tap. The sound of water gushing into the kettle jolted him back to earth. There was no point in spending the money until he knew how much he had won. He glanced at the clock. The news would be on in ten minutes, and then he would know just how rich he was.

'Tonight three ticket holders have all six lottery numbers, winning an estimated £6.6 million each ...' That was the only news the Whites were interested in. Ken switched off the TV with the remote and fell back into his chair. He jumped to his feet almost immediately to move the telephone from Sheila's grasp as he caught sight of her moving her hand towards the receiver.

'Hang on, love. Before you start telling the world,

let's get our facts right,' said Ken. 'If we really have won all that money there's a lot to be sorted before we let people know.'

'Of course we've won – it said so on the news. What more proof do you want? Pass me that phone.'

Ken shook his head and turned to the back of the ticket. There was a number to call for anyone who thought they had won a large amount. 'Hold your horses at least until I've spoken to somebody at Camelot,' he said crossly, squinting as he read the numbers before tapping them into the phone. He listened to the recorded message that greeted him on the line. It was a woman's voice.

'I have to say yes when she gets to the bit about big winners,' he whispered to Sheila, holding his hand over the mouthpiece. Sheila frowned and shook her head at him. He wasn't making sense.

'Yes,' said Ken into the phone, smiling and nodding his head towards her. But he too began to frown as he realised the line had gone dead. He held the receiver in front of him and stared at it for a moment before replacing it on the handset.

'They've bloody cut me off,' he said as he pressed REDIAL and waited to be reconnected. 'Now I've got to listen to the whole message again until she gets to my bit.' They sat in silence as Ken waited for the prompt.

'If you think you are a big winner, say yes now,' said the woman's voice.

'Yes,' said Ken, speaking directly into the mouthpiece. He looked at Sheila and held his hand over the phone again. 'It'll trip me through to an operator now,' he explained.

But the line went dead once more. 'Pass me that phone,' said Sheila, holding out her hand.

Ken sighed and handed it to her. She was equally unsuccessful.

An hour later they still hadn't been able to get through to an operator, despite both yelling down the phone at the prompt. Ken hurled himself back into his chair.

'Let's get hold of the boys,' said Ken, exasperated by his failed attempts to get through to Camelot. He had been unsure about sharing their news until it was confirmed. But his frustration at not being able to get through somehow helped convince him that the ticket in his hand really was worth millions of pounds.

He wanted to tell his boys – he wanted them to be a part of this. David, his eldest, would be home soon. He was staying with them at the moment while he sorted out some problems he was having with his wife, Lynne. Stephen would probably be at home. The little'n, Richard, was on a long-haul job in Spain. His wife, Julie, would know how to get hold of him. Sheila set to work on the telephone, rounding up her sons before ringing her relatives to share the news.

Ken pulled back the cuff on his shirt and looked at his watch. It was half-past two in the morning. He glanced at the half-empty cups of tea scattered on the coffee table and decided to leave them there until the morning. Sheila and David shouting 'yes' into the telephone in perfect unison interrupted his thoughts. They still hadn't got through.

'I'm off to my bed,' said Ken.

'You're what?' exclaimed David. 'You can't go to bed.'

Rachel Halliwell

'Oh, bugger it,' said Ken. 'I'll try again in the morning.' He picked up the lottery ticket from the coffee table and put it in his back trouser pocket. 'This,' he laughed, 'is coming with me.'

Ken pulled back the sheets and slid the ticket beneath his pillow before climbing into bed. He smiled as he heard Sheila shout out 'yes' yet again. He hadn't seen her this animated in ages. It had to be ten years since she had spent so long, bar time asleep, away from the pages of one of her books and the chair that seemed a part of her now.

It was good to get a glimpse of the old Sheila again. She had infuriated him by promising the best part of a million pounds to her family and friends, but that was Sheila all over. If it really was true – if he had won the £6.6 million pounds the newscaster had said – then she would get to hand out a small fortune to whomever she chose. Sheila would make sure of that, and he would have to accept it.

Sheila always had to get her way and always would. He remembered her as she was when they first met. What a hold she had on him then. Her beauty had tantalised him. Her wit and humour had kept him close when her bad temper and constant criticism threatened to drive him away.

Now, her beauty was gone, the slender girl he would yearn to make love to replaced by an overweight woman who could hardly walk after years of inactivity. They shared a bed each night, but there had been no intimacy now for four years. Before that, sex, or even just a cuddle, was an infrequent event and always because Sheila felt like it.

6

His own sons, even her mother, had openly questioned why he stayed with Sheila. But however hard done to he might feel at times, he could always remember the happiness she brought him in their first years together, and the love she inspired in him then remained. Above all she was the mother of his children.

Ken reached under his pillow and felt for the ticket. It was still there. It was incredible to think that it was worth so much money, yet had another set of numbers been drawn it would have been destined for the bin. Only as a boy had he known a piece of paper hold such value, when ration coupons were worth more than the paper money in his father's wallet.

Ken White was born in 1931, the youngest of five sons with five sisters. He grew up in a rambling seven-bedroom house in Newport in South Wales. The family had its own dance band – The Renaldo Swingtimers. Most Saturday nights their father would return from the local club with his friends for a fish-and-chip supper with the Swingtimers providing the entertainment. Up to eighty people had been known to file into their massive living room, singing and dancing into the early hours.

The Second World War meant conscription for the older White sons, but the band continued on a smaller scale. War brought a wider audience. Each weekend they visited army camps to entertain the troops.

The war brought hardship for many families, but the Whites always seemed to have jam on the table and decent clothes on their backs. Their trips to the army barracks made them minor celebrities among the soldier lads, who always sent parcels for their mother filled with butter, jam, milk and sugar – things that not even ration coupons could buy. She would then trade food coupons for clothing coupons, keeping her family well dressed.

For Ken it was an exciting time. Air raids meant that school was often abandoned. Instead of taking cover, he and his friends would race from the school gates to the Bristol Channel sea wall and watch the air battles being fought out in the skies above them. The massive static water tanks, which stored the water for fighting fires, were their swimming pools. Lads roamed in gangs, making bomb sites their playgrounds, and Ken always seemed to be around the ringleaders. There had been many moments as an adult when Ken had stood on the banks of the River Usk, which surges through the town, and recalled with horror times when they swam across it to fight rival gangs on the dockside opposite. Their opponents would hurl broken bricks at them as they reached the water's edge to try to stop them from landing. Their mission was to land, fight the other gang members, and then swim back to safety.

Ken's father Richard's main trade was as a master carpenter. He also ran a haulage firm and never missed a business opportunity if he spotted a way to make money for his family. He was a regular face at the docks when ships were being broken up and would reclaim any good wood he could find. He made the cross that was later put on his own grave from oak he reclaimed from the *Empress of France*. For twenty years it lay in an old cupboard on the top floor of the house – a cupboard none of the children dared even walk past because they knew what was inside.

While he made his living from carpentry and his work as a wheelwright – making and repairing wheels on horse-drawn carts – Richard's true love was fretwork. He would spend hours locked in his workshop at the house making intricate jewellery boxes decorated with miniature ballerinas. During the war years his children were never short of toys. Beneath the Christmas tree were hand-crafted doll's houses and garage sets he made himself throughout the year.

Richard White instilled the work ethic in all his sons at an early age. While Ken's friends enjoyed Saturday-morning trips to the cinema, he would be working at his father's yard putting together bundles of firewood to deliver to the houses in neighbouring streets. He never complained or tried to duck out of working – respect rather than fear meant he would never question any of the tasks his father set. Richard was not a man to be argued with and had the ability to make a grown man back down before him with a simple change in the tone of his voice.

He had physical strength and knew how to use it – he simply chose not to. But he did teach Ken how to use his fists to defend himself if he needed to after seeing him, aged six, crying to his older brothers about being bullied in the streets.

'Never show fear to anyone – unless it's a woman,' he warned Ken as he lifted him on to a chair in the kitchen. 'I'm going to teach you how to box so you never need to come crying to your brothers again.'

After that first lesson he held a gleaming

half-crown in front of Ken's eyes and promised it to him the day he managed to bloody his nose. Two days later Richard proudly handed that coin to his son before searching his pockets for a handkerchief to wipe the blood that poured from his nose.

Years later Ken would be called to his own youngest son's school to answer to the headmistress after Richard, aged five, made a classmate's nose bleed. Ken was told that their main concern was what Richard said when he was reprimanded. He told his teacher he had been following his father's advice – hit first and ask questions later. Ken happily admitted saying just that. 'I'd rather he got in trouble at school than be bullied,' he told her. 'Kids are affected by bullying for the rest of their lives – it'll not happen to one of mine.'

Ken himself was never bullied again. He was beaten black and blue many times but took great pride in the fact that anyone who took him on always came off at least as badly as he did – and never picked a fight with him again.

As he entered adulthood Ken found himself a reluctant champion for those who couldn't, or wouldn't, stand up for themselves the way he did. It was a role he would play throughout his adult life.

As a teenager in the army he witnessed much bullying – something he thought he was leaving behind in the school yard. When the war ended, prison camps were turned into army bases for conscripts like Ken whose living quarters were Spartan huts heated by raging coke fires at either end. Each hut saw self-imposed segregation – the southerners down at one end and the Welsh and Scottish lads teaming up with the northern boys at the other. In Ken's hut was a youngster who today would be described as having learning difficulties. Often, in the evenings, he would stand on a chair and sing at the northern end of the billet. One night he was called over to the southern end, where a gang of cockney soldiers hauled him up on to a chair and demanded he entertain them.

Ken watched from the top end of the hut as the teasing and jostling became more sinister. Soon the boy was being slapped and pinched – then they began brushing their red-hot cigarette ends to make him jump. As he began to weep, Ken could stand it no longer.

'Get down now, lad,' he called over to the boy.

That was just what the ringleader, a giant of a man, was waiting for. He charged over to Ken, rolling up his shirtsleeves. The fight that followed landed them both in the infirmary, but there was a mutual respect as well as distance between them from then on. As for the boy he stood up for – he followed Ken around like a lapdog for the rest of his time there.

Conscription was no hardship for Ken – he thrived on the camaraderie, and discipline and respect had always been part of his life. But it was the army that Ken would later resent for robbing him of the opportunity to become friends with the man he aspired to be like all his life – his father. When he received the call to his base in Buckinghamshire to say his father, sick with pneumonia, was dying, Ken hitchhiked his way home. It took him seven hours to get there, and Richard had died two hours earlier. Ken had just twenty-four hours' leave to say goodbye at his funeral. He had always envisaged himself spending Saturday nights stood at the bar in their local talking man to man when he returned to Civvie Street. Instead, their relationship ended without them ever making the transition from father and son to friends. One of his greatest regrets would always be that he wasn't there, at his dad's bedside, the night he died. His only option was to throw himself back into army life – never finding enough time alone to grieve or dwell on what might have been until his own sons became men.

When Ken left the army in 1952, after two years as a driver, he had money in the bank, his own car and an eye for a good-looking girl – of which there seemed no shortage. He missed out on being part of the first generation of postwar teenagers, too busy working for his father or immersed in army life. But that was no bar to his being part of rock and roll. He worked hard all week driving lorries for local firms. The weekends were spent down at the drill hall. There frenzied jiving was often the prelude to meaningless sex with a new breed of girl who had little care for the virginity her older sister had clung to so valiantly. Ken's mother despaired at her youngest son, who appeared unperturbed by his behaviour of the night before.

'When will you meet a nice girl and bring her home to meet me?' she would ask as he scowled back at her, nursing his hangover. 'Maybe then you won't feel so sick on a Sunday morning.'

It was at a drill-hall dance that Ken first met Sheila. The town's 'clippies' – bus conductresses – always made it to the dance each Saturday night. This was their chance to show the young men they had flirted with through the week, handing out tickets in their dowdy uniforms, how good they could look. Sheila was one of them.

'Hands off that one, Snowy,' a lad called Philip advised him one night. Ken's pal Victor was making a play for one of the clippies, which meant he had danced with her friend, Sheila Lord, a couple of times as moral support.

'Which one?' asked Ken, instantly searching for sight of the last woman he had danced with. He remembered her name as his eyes rested on her – sat across the dance floor tapping cigarette ash on to the floor.

'Sheila Lord. I'm going to tap that one tonight.'

'Are you now?' said Ken, setting his pint of bitter down beneath his chair and rising to his feet. 'See you then.' He smiled at Philip and headed in Sheila's direction.

Before that conversation he had barely noticed this girl – his thoughts and plans for that evening involved the redhead who had smiled at him as he queued for drinks. Now he took Sheila's hand and led her to the dance floor, hellbent on leaving with nothing less than a date for the following night.

'You not dancing?' he called out over the music in his rival's direction, grinning as two of Philip's friends grabbed an arm each to hold him back. He turned back to Sheila and spun her around to the music. She was a beauty – tall and slim with a fabulous smile. He was amazed he hadn't noticed her before.

Ken looked at his watch. The film *Gone with the Wind* would be starting soon and there was still no sign of Sheila. It started to rain. He was about to make his way into the cinema foyer to shelter when he caught sight of Joan, Sheila's younger sister, crossing the road towards him.

He knew then that Sheila wouldn't be coming.

'I'm to see her at home then,' he said, holding the cinema door open for Joan as the spots of rain turned into a heavy shower.

'Sorry, Ken,' said Joan. 'She says you're to come back with me. Our dad's not gone down the club yet. He said he'd wait for you if you wanted to go for a pint with him.'

'Christ, Sheila, I haven't seen you for days and all you're interested in is that bloody book,' he yelled as he walked into her mother's sitting room.

He had never raised his voice to her before, and Sheila was visibly shaken by his tone. She soon composed herself and stared hard into his eyes, using them to express the defiance burning inside her. She raised her eyebrows and smiled before returning her gaze to her book.

'Dad's waiting – he'll have a drink with you,' she said.

'I don't want to have a drink with your dad. I'm supposed to be courting you, not your bloody father.'

'You know what you can do if you don't like it,' said Sheila, as she appeared to continue reading. Ken turned, ready to walk away, exasperated by her attitude. 'Shut the door on your way out,' she called after him.

Ken slammed it as hard as he could and went looking for her father.

'Why do you put up with it, lad?' asked Sheila's father, Joe, as they waited for their drinks.

Ken shrugged his shoulders and smiled. He had no answer for him because he didn't know himself. Their first few dates had been great. They had gone to the cinema, been dancing or taken romantic walks down by the sea. Sheila was beautiful, witty and bright. He had quickly fallen in love with her and was certain she felt the same.

They spent much of their time apart. Ken was working as a long-distance lorry driver and she worked shifts on the buses. When their time off coincided, Ken would be buzzing for hours before they were due to meet, desperate to spend time alone with her.

But she began to turn up late for their dates. Then she stopped turning up at all, sending Joan in her place to make excuses for her. She would have a headache or an upset stomach and would want to stay at home in the warm. Then Joan would tell him that Sheila just didn't feel like going out that night. He would find her at home sat on the settee with her legs tucked under her and a packet of fags on the table beside her. She would look up from her book and smile that wonderful smile of hers. A quick kiss was all she could spare him – the pages of her latest paperback demanded her full attention. He would leave the house with her father and spend their date with him down at the local club.

Sheila had a hold over him. He didn't understand why or how she managed to make up for giving him so little at times. Perhaps she was the ultimate challenge – a woman bored with her life before it had a chance to get started properly. They courted for four years, then Ken asked Sheila to marry him.

* * *

Three months after the wedding, Sheila conceived their first child. Ken watched in awe as her body changed to accommodate the new life growing inside her. He had always found her attractive, but now she appeared more beautiful than ever.

He was still spending many nights away from home as he drove long distances in his lorry – something he warned her would never change. 'It's in my blood, Sheila. I near enough cut my teeth on a steering wheel,' he told her, remembering how his father taught him to drive in one of his own vehicles.

Sheila seemed happy. Ken earned good money and would provide a comfortable life for her and the baby when it arrived. She enjoyed her space – it gave her time alone to read without his complaints of the lack of attention she gave him when she became absorbed in one of her books.

The nights they were together they lay in each other's arms. Ken would rest his hand gently on her growing belly and stroke it as he felt his unborn child moving inside her. He had never loved her more.

Six months into the pregnancy Sheila visited the hospital for an antenatal appointment. Ken was working locally that week, so he returned home at lunchtime expecting Sheila to be full of news of how the baby was developing. She wasn't there.

Sheila's parents lived just a few doors away, so he made his way there. They hadn't seen her. Ken knew something was wrong. Sheila was predictable – she never ventured far from home, and if she had to go out would return as quickly as possible.

An inexplicable sense of dread engulfed him as he walked the streets around their home. He kept telling himself he would see her around the next corner, but deep down he knew he wouldn't. He made his way to his sister's house to see if she had seen Sheila.

'Ken – thank God you're here,' said Frances as she opened the door.

She showed him into the kitchen, where Sheila was sitting at the table, her cup of tea cold and untouched in front of her. Her face was ashen, her eyes red from crying. She looked up at him and her body began to shake. 'Oh, Ken,' she wept. 'The baby – there's something wrong with our baby.'

Ken crouched down so he could hold her without her getting out of the chair. She was trembling so much he doubted she would be able to stand anyway.

'What is it, love? What's happened?' he asked gently. She sobbed into his chest, unable to speak.

Ken looked at Frances, who shook her head and looked to the floor. 'Come into the hall,' she whispered.

Ken gently prised himself away from Sheila. 'I'll be back in a minute, love.'

Outside in the hallway Ken tried to blank out the gentle moaning now coming from the kitchen as Frances explained that the baby was going to die. Sheila had been told that morning that the child she was carrying had a brain abnormality. It would continue to grow inside her for another three months and Sheila would go into labour and give birth naturally, as in any normal pregnancy. But within minutes of its birth the baby would die.

'There must be something they can do,' said Ken as he leant against the wall, his head spinning.

'There's nothing, Ken – nothing at all they can do. They told her the baby was incompatible with life.'

'What the bloody hell does that mean – incompatible with life? How can a baby grow inside a woman for all that time and then die when she's barely had a chance to hold it? It doesn't make sense to me.'

'Ken,' said Frances firmly. 'It doesn't matter what words they use to explain it or how cruel it might seem – it's going to happen. We've just got to help that girl through this the best we can.'

Ken pictured Sheila as he left the house that morning – brushing her hair and putting on some make-up ready for her visit to the hospital. That image was replaced with one of her sat alone in the doctor's room as he told her the terrible news. Then it dawned on him – she would have been on her own when she heard details of the ordeal ahead of her.

'Bloody hell – she was on her own,' he said, his grief temporarily replaced with anger. 'They told her something like that when she was on her own.'

He marched back into the kitchen and took her back in his arms. 'You're not on your own now, love. You don't have to do this on your own.'

From that day Sheila barely spoke, and her eyes were permanently raw from crying. They moved into her parents' home and she refused to leave the house. Ken came off the long-distance work and took a job at the local foundry. It was regular hours and meant he was home each evening to be with Sheila. He hated every minute of it, but he knew he had to be there for her.

The morning she went into labour she didn't tell Ken that her waters had broken. She waited until he had left for work before telling her mother it was time to go to the hospital. When Ken returned home that evening the baby had been born and died just as the doctors had said. All that was left for him to do was arrange the funeral. The baby boy was buried, without a name, in a shared grave. Ken wondered if Sheila would ever smile again.

'We'll have another lad, Sheila,' he said, squeezing her hand as she lay motionless in the bed, the covers pulled up tightly around her. She stared straight ahead, her eyes dull and lifeless.

He wanted to hold her as he had the day they had heard that the baby would die. He wanted to feel her tears on his neck again as she had clung to him and he had comforted her. He wanted to feel needed – to know that his words could soothe her just a little, as they had that day.

But right now the only thing he could do for her was to leave her alone. He felt useless and alone as he walked out of the room.

David was born almost a year later. Ken and Sheila clung to each other and wept as, together, they wrapped their arms around him. There had been times after their first baby died when Ken wondered if his wife would ever let him into her bed, let alone her life again. Gradually she had returned, physically anyway, to her family – leaving the bedroom she had retreated to for longer periods. When she discovered she was pregnant, she had been unable to enjoy a moment of it. Nothing the doctors said could convince her that this baby was normal. It was only when she awoke the morning after his birth and felt his sweet-smelling breath on her cheek that she believed he was hers to keep.

Ken felt deep pride. Here was a son he could nurture and teach the way his own father had raised him. He would take this helpless baby and show him how to fend for himself. He was amazed a child could move him so much. He thanked God he had helped make Sheila smile again.

Stephen's birth two years after that followed similar trauma for Sheila. Again she had been terrified she would lose her baby before she had chance to love it. Ken had been less frightened – David's arrival had helped him accept that the first death had been an unlucky fluke of nature. Sheila was besotted with Stephen and wouldn't let him out of her sight, while he refused to settle for anyone but her. She was exhausted. Stephen was a poor sleeper, and Ken had gone back on the road within an hour of his birth. He had returned to his lorry a month after their first baby died and they had spent more time apart than together ever since.

To Ken their way of life was natural, and he was certain Sheila felt the same. He was bringing in a good wage, and she was happy with her two boys to care for.

But after Stephen, Sheila suffered one miscarriage after another. Each time they learnt she was pregnant they refused to get excited – convinced the baby would die within the first few months of conception. It was only when Richard was born that the doctors discovered a tear in her womb. Ken always thought of his youngest son as his miracle child – a baby who was so determined to live that he survived with the odds stacked against him. Sheila had been in and out of hospital throughout the pregnancy, and they had been warned many times she would lose him.

'You'll go a long way, little'n,' he told Richard as he gently swung his newborn son from side to side, his arms acting as a cradle. The baby's angry screams gradually subsided and his eyelids began to droop. As he drifted off to sleep Ken smiled at his baby.

'I'm here for you, lad,' Ken whispered in his tiny ear. 'Whenever you need me, I'm here.'

As their children grew so did the distance between Ken and Sheila. Ken worked away most weeks, and at the weekends he would take his boys for trips to the seaside or fishing to give her a break.

They rowed furiously, but there was still an intense passion between them. Ken had grown used to Sheila's sharp tongue long ago. But the way she spoke to him, and sometimes lunged at him, never failed to shock those close to them.

'You know, if you were a man our Ken would have punched you by now,' warned his sister Mavis after witnessing their latest fight. Sheila had hurled a saucepan at him after he arrived home late for dinner. Now Ken was cooling off down at the pub.

'If your good-for-nothing brother spent a bit more time at home –'

'But Sheila, he works hard making good money for you and the boys,' Mavis interrupted.

'Keep out of it, Mavis,' warned Sheila. 'You don't know what it's like.'

While his family, and sometimes even her own, openly questioned why he tolerated Sheila's rages, Ken remained devoted to her.

Her refusal to socialise frustrated him – not just because they rarely went out together but because on the few occasions when they did she captivated everyone around her. That sharp tongue of hers could be as entertaining as it was hurtful, and she had the most infectious laugh he had ever heard.

Most times he could put up with being told how useless he was because he was certain she didn't mean it. It was life she was angry with – not him. She had never tried to hide that displeasure she felt towards the world around her. Ken's mistake had been to think he could change that for her.

All those babies she carried then lost had caused as much damage to her mind as they had her heart, he was sure of that. That pain must have convinced her she was right.

He loved her and he was certain she loved him just as deeply. If those who questioned the sense in his staying with her could see the tenderness and passion they shared in private they would understand.

Ken managed to walk away from nearly all their rows, even the ones where she screamed and lashed out with her fists or whatever lay close to hand. But just once he hit back.

He had arrived home from a trip far later than he had expected. The traffic had been a nightmare. The kitchen was warm and inviting. David and Stephen were playing with their toy cars on the table, and Richard was sleeping peacefully in his cradle beside them. Sheila had her back to him, washing pots at the sink. He stood at the door and watched in silence – he felt glad to be home.

'Where the bloody hell have you been?' screamed Sheila, sensing his presence and spinning around to face him. 'Well?' she glared at him, her hands on her hips.

'I got held up, the traffic –'

'What's the point of having a husband when he can't even be bothered to get home for his supper? I promised the boys you'd be home to share a meal with us tonight. You're useless, Ken, bloody useless.'

Ken walked slowly towards her. He so wanted to retrieve the situation, to be a part of that tranquil scene he had only had chance to watch. She had turned her back to him again. He placed his hand gently on her shoulder, inviting her to turn back towards him and let him hold her close. 'I'm sorry, love.'

Sheila turned and shrugged his hand off her. Ken didn't see the cup in her hand full of the dregs from the bottom of the sink. He just felt the cold, dirty water as it slopped over his face.

Anger took hold of him. He tried to focus on his sons, watching just feet away. Their had stopped playing, and they watched him intently. They weren't usually audience to their parents' rows.

Ken sat down on the chair closest to where Sheila was standing. She grinned as he took a handkerchief from his pocket and wiped his face. Then he grabbed her around the waist and pulled her down in one swift movement so that she lay face down across his lap. He lifted up the skirt of her dress and pulled down her underwear, exposing her backside. Then he raised his hand and brought it down hard, spanking her like a naughty child. 'If you,' he said, timing his words to coincide with each fall of his hand, 'are going, to act, like a child, then I, will treat you, like, a child.'

Sheila began to cry. The mixture of pain and the humiliation of being spanked in front of her children was too much for her. Ken threw her skirt back over her and pushed her back to her feet before rising and walking calmly out of the room. Sheila pushed past him as she fled, weeping, to the bedroom. David and Stephen giggled together before returning to their game.

The family moved to a new council estate built at the bottom of Twm Balam mountain. It was the 1960s and the authorities had a new policy of putting a wide range of age groups on these estates, the idea being that the communities which developed would support the people living in them.

Ken hated it. The walls were thin, and most nights he was home he would have to listen to the violent, drunken rantings of his neighbour as he lashed out at his wife. One night Ken could stand it no longer and hammered on his neighbours' door.

'You leave her alone,' he warned the young man who swayed from side to side on the doorstep after returning from a heavy drinking session at the pub.

The lad knew Ken meant business. Ken was known by most as someone who rarely lost his temper, but when he did trouble quickly followed. The lad assured Ken that the rows would stop, and the couple moved off the estate a couple of weeks later.

From then on every woman having similar problems with her husband would run straight to Ken and Sheila for help. The first sign of trouble within the community and Snowy White, as Ken was always known, was called in to sort things out.

'I'm bloody sick of this,' he told Sheila. 'I feel like the bloody Godfather.'

Ken's brother-in-law, Trevor, was about to put his

house in Dewsland Park Road, in Newport, up for sale so Ken bought it off him. He and Sheila both loved the rambling Victorian terrace and felt sure they could make it their home for the rest of their lives. Sheila was in her element. Every time Ken returned from a long-haul trip, another room had been decorated or a new piece of furniture had been carefully chosen and placed in just the right spot. The boys had room to run and play, and the neighbours didn't expect him to sort out their domestic disputes. The Whites were happier than they had ever been.

'Sheila, love,' Ken called across the bedroom as he stared into his wardrobe. 'I can't find a clean shirt.'

Sheila turned the page of her book.

'I said I can't find my shirt. Have you done any washing this week?'

'What?' said Sheila, glancing up and then back down again.

'You've not done the washing again, have you, Sheila?' Ken strode over to the bed and snatched the book from her hand. 'Will you bloody listen to me, woman, and stop burying yourself in those damned books. Christ, when was the last time we even had a conversation, never mind you doing any housework?'

Sheila snatched the book out of his hand and found the page she had been reading. 'I just want to finish this chapter before I get the boys their breakfast.'

That's right – she would get the boys their breakfast and anything else they needed; she would never neglect them. But he could sing for whatever he needed from her. They hadn't had sex in months, and the house was thick with dust. He had spent the last two weekends cleaning the house, washing and ironing the family's clothes and cooking for them all while Sheila lay in bed reading.

He knew he should be thankful she wasn't neglecting the boys, but it was hard to accept that when the weekend came and he was around she would leave everything to him. Through the week she made sure the children got off to school clean and fed and then would return to her bed. She made no attempt to hide from him what she doing. Sheila wasn't frightened of what anyone thought of her, including Ken. But this was so unlike her. She had always been such a hard grafter, often working shifts at the hospital all night and then looking after her children during the day. The house had always been immaculate, and there was always food on the table when she knew he was coming home.

'What is it, Sheila? Are you ill, love?'

'I told you – I want to finish this chapter before I get their breakfasts. You'll have to wear a dirty shirt today. It won't kill you.'

'Oh, sod you, woman,' yelled Ken as he snatched yesterday's shirt from the back of the chair in front of the dresser.

He had planned to try to coax Sheila away from the house for a day out the next day, which was Saturday. Instead, he would be spending it doing housework again.

A couple of weeks later Sheila missed her period for the first time since Richard had been born. Convinced she was pregnant, she didn't know whether to be thrilled or terrified. Ken thought it might explain her recent behaviour. She returned from the doctor's bewildered; there was no baby.

Sheila never had another period. She was just

thirty-five and had started the menopause. She climbed aboard a hormonal rollercoaster which at that time had no form of treatment to help her through it.

Her doctor prescribed antidepressants as she spent more time in bed than out of it. She would make sure the children were washed and dressed before sending them to school and spend the hours before their return living her life solely through the characters in the books she devoured now more than ever before.

As far as Ken was concerned she was beginning to give up on life. The vibrant woman he once knew seemed to have gone, and he wondered if she would ever return.

In 1972 Ken was offered an office job in the North of England setting up a new transport depot. Sheila was getting worse. The tablets she was taking for depression seemed no help to her. Maybe a fresh start in a new part of the country, with him spending more time at home, would help.

They moved to Leigh, a small town near Wigan. But the transfer of the depot to the north-west was taking longer than expected, and Ken was spending more time in Wales than with his family.

'Christ Almighty, Ken, this was supposed to be the start of a new life for us here,' said Sheila, the tears streaming down her face. 'I'm spending more time alone, not less.'

Ken was shocked. He wasn't used to seeing her look so helpless and needy. 'It won't be for much longer,' he said, trying to reassure her.

'I'm lonely, Ken. I don't know anybody here. The children are getting older – they've got friends of their own. They don't need me the same. You've got to do something.'

Ken grabbed the evening paper from the table and turned to the Situations Vacant section. 'Right – there's a job here for a transport foreman. If it's what you want, I'll get that.'

Sheila wiped her eyes with her hands and nodded her head.

Ken went for an interview the following day and returned with a new job, as he had promised. Instead of landing the foreman's job, he was given the transport manager's post.

'I told you I'd put things right,' he told her.

'I just need to spend more time with you – I'll get better then.'

Ken took her hand and squeezed it between both of his. 'Of course you will, love.'

Ken's new job kept him away as much as any other he'd had. He was sent to college in Prestatyn to learn how to use a computer before he could begin to run a fully computerised office. He was twice the age of the other students but quickly discovered that his brain was just as sharp as theirs.

Meanwhile, Sheila was still spending her weekdays alone, with Ken home only at the weekends. She had had a job at a nearby hospital but left after a few months. She never gave a reason other than that it didn't suit her any more.

She refused to leave the house. Ken took over the household chores and found his own way of dealing with the virtual end of their physical relationship. Until then, the only real contact he had with women was with Sheila and his female relatives. Now he was office-based instead of working on the road. Occasionally, the friendships that started at work developed into affairs. Sheila seemed to know instinctively that this was happening.

'You smell like one of the perfume counters at Debenhams,' she sniped as he slipped into bed in the early hours. He had taken his secretary for dinner and they had ended up taking a room in the hotel where they ate.

Ken had told Sheila he was going to a dinner-dance with people from work, and he had even asked her if she would join him. He had known she wouldn't – he had pleaded with her to go with him to countless events in the past but she had always refused.

Ken lay in silence, thankful for the darkness. There was no point in trying to explain why he smelt of another woman's perfume. Sheila wasn't that stupid.

'Do what you like, Ken – I really don't care,' said Sheila coldly, turning away from him and on to her side. Then she turned her head in his direction. 'Just don't ever bring any of them home with you. Do you hear me?'

'I hear you,' said Ken, turning his back to hers. She knew and she didn't care – he saw no point in wasting any more time feeling guilty.

Ken awoke and for a moment wondered why there was a crumpled piece of paper in his hand. He sat up in bed and opened his palm. Then he remembered. Sheila was sleeping soundly beside him. She wouldn't be wanting her cup of tea so early this morning – she probably hadn't been in bed very long and would sleep late. He climbed out of bed and put on his dressing gown. He had an important phone call to make.

Chapter Two

K EN PULLED A BOWL from out of the cupboard and filled it with cornflakes. He poured over the last of the milk. They had drunk so much tea last night there was barely enough left to cover them.

They should have been drinking champagne instead of tea, he thought. It might have felt more real then, more exciting. But they had been too busy trying to get through to Camelot to go out and buy some. In fact, the idea hadn't even occurred to them. He'd never understood the fuss about the stuff himself, and Sheila wasn't a great fan.

He picked up his cup of tea from the kitchen worktop and carried his breakfast through to the lounge. It was 7.30 a.m. There was no point in trying to ring Camelot before nine.

David and Sheila were both still asleep upstairs. The half-empty cups of tea and overflowing ashtrays from the night before had been tidied away. Ken had expected them to be waiting for him. He opened a window to let out the stale air – despite thirty-nine years married to a heavy smoker he still couldn't get used to the smell of stale tobacco in a room.

He sat down and reached for the newspaper he

had picked up from the doormat on his way down. He placed his ticket on the page next to that week's winning numbers. They still matched.

Frustration hit him. When was this going to feel real? When would he know for sure that he had won, that he was rich? He stood up and walked to the window, staring out of it but not really seeing anything. It would feel real soon enough. When he held the cheque in his hand he was certain it would feel very real.

Ken smiled as he thought of how his utter conviction that he would one day win the lottery had provided so much amusement for his family and friends. He had spent £23 on tickets each week since it first started.

There was method in that figure – as there was in everything he did. He used to put £7 a week on the pools and had transferred that over. Then, when he saw there were five lines on each ticket he made that up to £10 – a round figure. David and Richard would also ask him to put five lines on for each of them, and Sheila had another three.

He bought the tickets from Cannings, the newsagent in the arcade next to the bus depot in Leigh, every Monday afternoon. It was just across the road from David's pine shop. At first the boys gave him the money by the Friday or Saturday, but they soon lost interest and stopped. Ken, superstitious by nature, couldn't bear to risk any of those numbers coming up and so continued with all twenty-three lines.

He had given up trying to explain that he was rarely that much out of pocket. Most weeks he would win at least £10. Still, he would be the one cracking the jokes now.

Yet now he had won – or at least it looked like he had won – he wondered if he had really been so certain that this would happen. After all, they say you have more chance of being run over by a bus. Maybe he had just said it to shut them up – which it hadn't.

Ken carried his empty bowl back into the kitchen and rinsed it clean before placing it on the draining board. He switched the kettle back on and wiped the worktop where he had splashed some water. He looked out on to the garden as he waited for the water to boil. They had a nice enough house, but it would be great to have somewhere bigger with more room for the grandchildren to play.

He wouldn't have to worry about a pension now. He had a few policies that would have given them enough to get by – although he'd had no intention of stopping work before he was seventy-five anyway. At sixty-four he was fit and healthy and still had his heavy goods licence. Only the other day he had driven one of Richard's wagons down to Bristol after two of his drivers called in sick. His lads would have always seen him right. Between them they could find him plenty of work. But now they wouldn't have to. Instead, he would be setting them up for the rest of their lives, and boy it felt good.

The prospect of being able to hand over a million pounds to each of his sons was the best thing about all this. Apart from loving them, it was the greatest gift he could imagine giving them. Instead of them giving him financial support in his dotage – something he never had a problem with because that was the way the Whites had always worked – he would be looking after them, in the first instance anyway. Once he handed them the money it would be up to them what they chose to do with it.

For Stephen the money would be a lifeline. His haulage firm had run into financial difficulties after several customers had run up bad debts. He was about to meet his own creditors to strike some kind of deal. The stress was a huge burden to him. Stephen hated being in debt. With a wife and four young children to provide for, he had cause to worry – their future had, until now, been uncertain.

Ken shook his head. He was doing it again – spending the money before he had got it. This could still all be some big mistake. He might not be able to do anything to help Stephen. His heart sank as he racked his brains trying to think of a way to help the lad. Cash had been tight for all the family in recent years, and none of them had access to the kind of money that he needed right now. They would pull together, as they always did in a crisis, but this was going to be a tough one.

The sinking sensation lifted again as he remembered the lottery. Of course he had won. He had the ticket in his pocket to prove it. The numbers in the paper were the same. The numbers on the news last night had been the same. All he needed now was for someone from Camelot to tell him what deep down he already knew.

He looked at the clock. Eight-thirty. Not long now. He heard the bathroom door slam upstairs. It had to be David – Sheila hated doors being slammed, something David had done since he was a little boy. No need to wonder what he would do with his million. David would turn it into another million within five years. Ken's eldest was a grafter with a good business head. He was already making a success of two shops, one selling electrical goods, the other pine furniture. Ken had been managing the pine shop for David for two years. Before that he had worked for Richard after his own haulage firm had gone bankrupt in 1987, leaving him unemployed. With a million pounds to play with there would be no stopping David.

And the little'n – well, he would spend his share on having the time of his life. Richard knew how to enjoy himself however much money he had in his pocket, and Ken knew he would take great pleasure in watching him spend his fortune. No doubt Richard would keep his haulage firm going and carry on driving his own vehicles. He was so like himself – always happiest out on the road.

David walked into the room. 'All right, Dad? Spending your millions, are you?'

'Not yet, lad,' Ken replied, grinning at his son. 'I'll wait until I get the cheque in my hand before I do that.' He still hadn't told David and his brothers how big a share of the money he planned to give them. He hadn't wanted to get them excited in case it was a mistake.

'Give over, Dad. It's yours.'

Ken nodded and smiled. 'Any sign of your mother?'

'She's just in the bathroom,' said David, glancing at the phone and then back at his father. 'Are you going to try that number again, Dad?'

Just then Sheila appeared at the door. She smiled at Ken.

'Come here and give us a cuddle,' he said, rising to

his feet and holding his arms open. They stood together, their arms tightly wrapped around each other.

'I still can't believe it, Ken. Have we really won all that money?' she said, her head buried in his chest.

'I think so, love. We'll know for sure when we speak to someone.' He gently pulled away from her. 'Are you ready for a cuppa?'

'Bloody hell,' she laughed. 'You've won millions of pounds on the lottery and I've seen you get more excited watching a game of rugby! Yes, I'll have a cuppa . . . for now. Then we'll get some champagne!'

'You're not usually that fussed about champagne,' said Ken.

'I've not usually turned into a millionairess overnight either,' giggled Sheila. 'I'll put the kettle on – you get on that bloody phone and find out what happens next.'

The recorded voice told Ken to say yes at the appropriate time. He did and was put straight through to an operator.

'Hello, love. I've been trying to get through to you all night.' Sheila and David watched him in silence. Ken smiled at them. They smiled back. Things were moving at last.

'It's Ken White here, love. I've got all six numbers from last night's lottery. Can you tell me what I need to do now?'

'Would you repeat to me the six numbers on your ticket?' said the voice on the end of the phone. The ticket was already in his hand. He read them to her.

'Now can you read me the code on the bottom of your ticket.' He read out the code.

'OK, Mr White. I'm now putting you through to Lucy Johnson. She will be able to help you further.'

'Just a minute, love –' She hadn't heard him. Ken was back on hold.

'Well?' said Sheila. 'What did they say?'

'Sh,' Ken snapped back. The line began to ring. He was through. She asked him to repeat the two sets of numbers.

'OK, Mr White. I can confirm that you are a potential winner,' she said.

'What does that mean? Potential winner?' Ken had expected something more concrete.

'It means that it very much looks as if you have won, but we need to confirm some more details. Now, have you signed the back of your ticket?'

He hadn't.

'Can I suggest you do that as a matter of urgency?'

'Pen – pen,' Ken mouthed at David, who disappeared into the kitchen to find one. He returned with a biro, and Ken scrawled his signature on the back of the ticket.

'Now I must ask you if you want to go public. You're probably aware that the media are very interested in lottery winners and they will be trying to find you as we speak. We can protect you from unwanted publicity if you wish.'

Ken thought for a moment. There was no point in trying to hide from journalists, he reasoned. They always find you in the end. 'That's all right, love – I'll go public.'

David walked back into the lounge with his coat on. Ken and Sheila stopped talking.

'Making plans for all that money, are you?' David

smiled at his father. 'I'm back off home – see if I can get Lynne to talk to me.'

'You make sure she does, son,' said Ken. Lynne had thrown David out of the house after a disagreement over their eldest daughter. He had been back to the house last night to try to smooth things over. Lynne hadn't believed him about the lottery – she wouldn't even let him in through the front door.

'See you, then,' said David, turning towards the door.

Ken and Sheila looked at each other. Sheila nodded.

'Wait a minute, son,' said Ken. 'Your mother and I have been talking.'

David took his coat off and sat down.

'It looks like we have got this money coming. It's just a case of a few formalities now.'

'I never doubted it, Dad.'

'Well, we've never cared that much for material things. There's only so much you can buy with that kind of money. We want to give some to you and your brothers – set you all up for life.'

David leant out of his chair to shake his father's hand. Then he kissed his mother on the cheek.

'Thanks, Dad. That's great.'

'You'll have a million each, lad.'

David sank slowly back into the chair. Ken watched intently as the implications of what he had said registered with David. He began to feel uncomfortable. He had to speak.

'I know you – you'll have made it into another million five years from now.'

'You don't have to do that, Dad. It's your ... I mean ... you don't need to –'

'Son,' Ken interrupted. 'We've talked about it. You three are our children – you always will be our children, however old you get. We couldn't spend that kind of money if we tried. To set you all up will give us more pleasure than spending it ever could.'

David leapt to his feet and shook Ken's hand again before reaching over to Sheila and hugging her.

'I'll look after it, you know,' he told them.

'We know you will, lad, we know you will,' said Ken. 'Now go and tell that wife of yours. We want this family together – there's no time for falling out now.'

Lucy Johnson arrived at the house at three o'clock. Again she warned Ken that the newspapers would all be keen to get an exclusive on the family but that she would do everything she could to protect them.

As they spoke, one freelance photographer was in his darkroom developing what he thought were exclusive photographs of Ken White, the latest lottery millionaire. He'd snapped him drinking a pint of bitter at his local, the Foundry, in Leigh.

Richard had been enjoying a lunchtime session there to celebrate his dad's big win with some friends. He had been in the same pub the night before after his dad had told him about the win – Richard had shouted their news to the other drinkers at the bar.

The landlord warned Richard that lunchtime that a photographer had been in asking questions about where he might find members of the family and would probably return.

In a corner of the pub Richard spotted a man a similar age to his father with the same snowy-white hair. They borrowed a pair of glasses for him from another drinker and promised him all the bitter he could drink if he would play along and pretend to be Ken White. When the photographer returned and was taken over to meet him, he had no idea he was the victim of a prank by the real Ken's youngest son.

Ken, Sheila and David were in the house to greet Lucy. Stephen had called round in the morning but had returned home to Susan to tell her that their money problems had been solved. David's attempt to resolve things with Lynne had failed. She had slammed the door in his face when he told her about the million pounds, telling him where he could stick his dad's money. Most of the town knew about the win now – yet Lynne still thought it was a trick to try to get her to sit down and talk to him.

'Here you are, love. You can take this off my hands now.' Ken laughed as he held out the ticket to Lucy.

She waved her hands back at him and shook her head. 'Sorry, Ken, no can do. That ticket is your responsibility until we get to Camelot's headquarters and it goes into the machine. We can't even confirm you are a winner until then.'

She explained that if she were to lose the ticket Camelot would be liable. Also there had been several attempts to fraudulently claim the jackpot. One man had bought a ticket the day after a draw with the winning numbers on it. He had then soaked it in water and ripped it up, claiming that his dog had tried to eat it. They soon discovered he was lying and the police were called in.

'Don't let that ticket out of your sight until we get

to London,' she warned him. 'It's worth a hell of a lot of money.'

'So does that mean he *has* won?' asked David. 'Surely you must be pretty certain by now?'

'Yes – he almost certainly has. It's just a matter of following procedure now.'

Ken was now certain he would be banking a cheque for £6.6 million on Tuesday morning. The win couldn't be confirmed any earlier because it was a Bank Holiday weekend.

At that moment the atmosphere changed from one of excited expectancy to sharp tension. Their lives were about to change beyond anything they had ever hoped or imagined for themselves or each other. It was frightening.

Lucy left to book herself into a nearby hotel, The Thistle, at Haydock. She had offered to put the family up there too so that they wouldn't be hassled by the press. Ken refused. The Whites didn't need protection – they could look after themselves. She arranged to meet them there that evening for dinner so that they could make arrangements for the trip to London the following day. Before she left she advised them to avoid answering the telephone or opening the door to anyone they didn't know.

'Why did you say we'd go public, Ken? We don't need the hassle,' said Sheila after she had gone. 'I don't want everybody knowing our business. It doesn't seem right.'

But Ken was adamant he was doing the right thing.

'Sheila, we've got eight grandchildren. You can't expect them to go to school and keep a secret as big as this. It wouldn't be fair to do that to the little ones.

Anyway, you know this town. Everyone'll know our business before long. If we give them what they want for the next week or so they'll leave us alone after that. I'll take the brunt of it – you don't need to worry.'

The atmosphere got more intense as the afternoon went on. The whole family gathered at the house – Richard and Julie, Stephen and Susan and David – to discuss the plans for the following day when they would travel to London together.

Knowing that the nation's media were trying to track them down didn't help. They began to feel trapped inside the house. Each time the doorbell or telephone rang they jumped, wondering if it was a journalist who had managed to track them down.

'We should close the curtains, then if anyone does call we can pretend we're out,' said Sheila.

Susan went to do as she suggested.

'Don't be so bloody stupid, Susan,' said Richard. 'You're being paranoid now.'

'I'm only doing as your mum said.'

'Just sit down, you silly woman.'

'Don't speak to me like that.' She turned to Stephen. 'Are you going to let him speak to me like that?'

Richard laughed. 'Come off it, Susan – since when have you needed our Stephen to fight your battles for you?'

Ken stood up. 'Why don't you all just shut your mouths and stop your bloody arguing,' he shouted. 'Otherwise you can all clear off home.'

The bickering was replaced with silence. Ken rarely raised his voice like that. Susan closed the curtains, glancing over at Richard as if to dare him to say something to her. Ken watched and felt relieved as Richard avoided looking at her. There was no love lost between those two, and normally Ken took little notice of their quarrels. But today being normal wasn't on the agenda.

That night Ken sat at the head of the table in the hotel restaurant, his wife on one side and Lucy on the other. His sons and their wives, all except Lynne, were seated before him. It felt good. Whatever problems each of them might encounter from now on, money wouldn't be one of them. How could it?

The lads were having a great time. The atmosphere seemed to have lifted again, helped along by the free-flowing beer and wine. Between them they were doing their best to wind up Lucy. They were always like this when they got together, but she was handling them well. It was just the way they were, and she wasn't taking offence.

Sheila was radiant. She had seemed nervous in Lucy's company at first but was much more relaxed now. She realised that Lucy was there to look after them and wouldn't push her into anything she didn't want to do. Ken tried to remember the last time Sheila had gone for a night out. He couldn't. He cast his mind back to the many quarrels they had had over her refusal to leave the house. She would get so upset, so angry. He had tried for years to understand why she was the way she was. The doctors had a name for it – they said she was agoraphobic and suffering from depression. But surely if you keep telling yourself you're depressed then you will be. If you rise above it, get on with your life, instead of locking yourself in your home for years on end, then you get better. The way she was now proved his point. Here she was, out of the house and enjoying herself. They had already talked about the holidays they would take – a world cruise first. It was like he'd said all along – she needed an interest, something to replace the gap left when the children grew up. If six million pounds wasn't going to get her interested in life, nothing was.

They left the hotel in the early hours and took taxis to their various homes. They would meet up with Lucy at Ken's in the morning.

Sheila sat down on the settee and took off her shoes. She started to unbutton her coat then stopped. 'I'm not coming tomorrow, Ken,' she said.

Ken looked at her. She was obviously exhausted.

'Oh, come on, Mum,' said David. 'It's going to be the biggest day of our lives. You've got to come.'

'He's right, Sheila, love,' said Ken. 'You'll regret it if you don't.'

Sheila found the energy to take off her coat and flung it over the back of her chair.

'I'm worn out. I can't face a long journey all the way to London. Anyway, it's not me they want to talk to – it's your dad. I'm stopping here. I don't want to leave the house empty.'

Ken stopped himself from any further attempts to change her mind. She had done well enough so far. She'd started to dig her heels in now; there was no point in trying to persuade her to change her mind. There would only be a row, and nobody wanted that. Maybe she would change her mind in the morning.

The doorbell rang at eleven the next morning. Stephen and Susan and Richard and Julie had arrived

an hour earlier and were sitting in the front room
waiting for the cars to arrive to take them to London.
Nobody spoke. They were frightened to in case they
started to argue. Ken had already warned them he
wasn't in the mood for the kind of bickering that
usually took place when the four of them were
together.

Lucy was in the kitchen talking to one of her
colleagues at Camelot on her mobile phone. It
seemed to ring every five minutes. Ken was in there
too, having one last go at making Sheila change her
mind.

The doorbell was a good excuse for her to get
away. 'It's probably our David forgotten his key,' she
said as she left the room.

David had gone back home again to try to talk to
Lynne. He was due back about now.

Ken went to join the others – they would be
leaving soon.

Sheila came back a few minutes later chuckling to
herself. 'It was a lad from one of the papers,' she said.
'*Daily Mirror*, I think. He wanted to know if this was
where Ken White the lottery millionaire lives.'

'Bloody hell – I thought nobody knew yet,'
exclaimed Ken.

Richard cleared his throat. 'Half of Leigh knows,
Dad. I got a bit excited when Julie rang me at the pub
last night and shouted the news across the bar.'

There was no point in being cross, Ken thought.
He'd have done the same himself. 'So where is he
now, this *Mirror* boy?' he asked.

'I told him I wasn't Mrs White – I was just
housesitting.' She began to roar with laughter. They
all joined in.

Ken grinned at his wife. He'd just got another glimpse of the old Sheila – the sharp, funny woman he was going to spend the rest of his life with. It was great to have her back.

'Can I bring you anything back from London, love?' Suddenly he really didn't mind her decision not to go.

'You could ask them to put the spare money in a bag for us.'

'What?' Ken exclaimed. 'It'd have to be a bloody big bag to keep £600,000-odd in.'

Sheila looked genuinely bemused. He laughed. She really had no idea what she was saying.

'I didn't realise,' she said. 'You can bring me back a little piece of jewellery – that'd be nice.'

He had bought her pieces of jewellery from all around the world when he had been on long-haul trips. The quality depended on how well things were going for the family at the time.

Ken kissed her on the cheek. 'I'll do that, my love. Just think – it'll be the first thing we ever buy with our winnings.'

They waved to Sheila as they pulled away from the house. She was peeping out from behind the net curtains, anxious not to be seen by the neighbours. Ken sat in the front passenger seat of the Ford Mondeo sent by Camelot to take them to London. Richard and Susan were in the back with Lucy. He'd put David in the other car, a Ford Cavalier, with Stephen and Susan. If he'd put the other two in with them there would probably have been a fist-fight in the car before they reached Birmingham. They were at each other's throats at every opportunity, and Ken still didn't understand why. David was fine whoever you put him with – he'd been the family go-between all his life.

Lucy felt like an old friend. She made them feel comfortable and important at the same time.

'I'll tell you what, love. I had twenty-two other lines,' said Ken. 'I haven't checked any of them yet.' He had – none of them were winners.

'That's all right, Ken. I'll just ring through to the office to check if there are any big winners coming up from where you bought your tickets.'

She rang a colleague. 'No, Ken. You're only getting about six million.' No one was disappointed.

Lucy pressed the button on her phone to disconnect her call and stared at it, deep in thought. 'Ken? Can I just check that ticket a minute? Where is it?'

'Right here where I always keep it – in my arse pocket. What do you want to see it for?' he asked as he passed it to her.

'Ken – you've marked the ticket. You've ticked off each number in ink.'

'So?'

'It's invalid. My God – the ticket's invalid. You shouldn't have done that.'

Ken jerked his head round and strained to face her. 'What are you saying . . .?' He felt sick.

She laughed. 'At last,' she said with glee. 'Gotcha!'

Ken laughed back. So she had.

The cheque presentation would be held the next day at Camelot's headquarters in Leicester Square. It would be followed with a press conference at the Waldorf. The family was checked into rooms at the

Portland Hotel. Camelot was still trying to keep the White family away from the press. If they'd put them straight into the Waldorf the pack would have been straight on to them.

Ken lay on the bed and stared at the ceiling. He'd slept in many hotel bedrooms during his years on the road. Most times he would fall into bed exhausted after a long drive, anxious to get enough sleep to revive him for another trek the next day. Things had changed. He was too fired up to feel tired. Things had moved quickly since he got in touch with the lottery people. Little more than twenty-four hours later and he was in London ready to collect a cheque that would change all their lives for ever.

He leant over to the telephone on the bedside table and dialled his home number. Sheila answered.

'We're here, love. We've all arrived safely. How are you?'

'I'm fine, Ken. Just hurry home with that cheque!'

That evening they joined Lucy and two of her colleagues, Susan Harris and Elaine Jeffers, in the hotel restaurant. The lads and their wives had been indulging in the champagne left in their rooms by Camelot. Ken just wanted a decent pint of bitter.

'You know, Ken, we run a sweep in the office,' said Elaine. She laughed. 'The winner is the first one to get into bed with one of the new millionaires.'

Ken looked at his watch. It was twenty to midnight. 'Well, love. You'll have won that sweep in another twenty minutes.' Everyone laughed as Ken drained the last of his pint. 'I'll just have another half and then I'm off to my bed. Busy day tomorrow.'

Lucy nodded to a waiter who was clearing away ready for the next day. They were the last people in the restaurant. He came over but told them the beer pumps had been switched off. The only beer they could offer Ken was in a bottle.

'Oh, forget it,' said Ken, rising to his feet. He was amazed that such a huge hotel in the capital city couldn't serve him a pint of bitter. 'I'll get my beauty sleep instead,' he said. 'I want to look good for my public.'

Ken took one last look at the ticket before he placed it under his pillow. He would be glad to see the back of it now. Looking after it had become a burden. Now he was sure he had won he felt as though he might as well have the millions in cash beneath his head: the responsibility felt the same. A few more hours and he would have his cheque. He was exhausted. He closed his eyes and waited for sleep to clear his mind. He didn't have to wait very long.

Chapter Three

THE RESTAURANT WAS BUSY. The sound of cutlery clinking against china dishes filled the room as tourists and business people ate breakfast. The atmosphere was in stark contrast to the night before. Then the lights were dimmed and soft music played in the background. This morning, sun streamed through the elegantly draped windows that lined one side of the room. There was no music to soften the busy chatter of the people seated around them.

Many of the people in the room would be preparing for business deals worth millions of pounds, mused Ken.

'I'll bet we're the only people here doing a deal that'll see us taking home a cheque for £6.6 million,' said David, as though Ken had spoken his thoughts aloud.

That was so like David, Ken thought. Everything was a deal that went either right or wrong. He liked that about him – it reaffirmed his belief that this money would help him reach great heights in the business world.

For a moment Ken felt incredibly isolated. Sure, he had most of his family seated around him, and there must have been at least a hundred people beyond them in the room. But while they knew what the day had in store, whether it was sightseeing or high-powered meetings, today he was stepping into the great unknown. It was daunting.

All he knew for certain was that after breakfast the cars would return to take them to Camelot's offices in Leicester Square, where the ticket would be validated and the cheque handed over. From there they would go to the Waldorf Hotel for a press conference.

This press conference was the part that concerned him. All doubts that there was any mistake over the money had gone, and he had picked up plenty of cheques in his time. That would be easy.

But he had never dealt with the media before. He had seen press conferences in films and on the television, and those scenes offered no reassurance. The reporters always came across as being so aggressive – firing questions and flashing their cameras in what looked like little less than an organised brawl.

'Have you thought about what you'll say to the reporters, Ken?' asked Julie. She must have noticed he had withdrawn from the excited banter at the table. She was a good girl – always concerned about the people around her.

'No, love,' said Ken, smiling warmly at her. She took his hand and squeezed it. 'You know me – I'll take it in my stride.'

Ken didn't believe in preparing for things he knew nothing about. He would answer their questions honestly and pose for whatever photographs they wanted. The only thing he did understand about journalists was that there was no point in holding anything back from them. He'd read enough copies of the *News of the World* to know that. He would tell them everything necessary for them to write their stories – then they would have no need to dig around looking for dirt.

Lucy joined them at the table. 'How is everyone this morning?' she asked brightly. 'All ready?'

Ken nodded, and the rest followed his lead.

'Well, I'll just finish my coffee and then we'll get in the cars. The most exciting part of all this is about to begin.'

Throughout the drive to the offices the conversation focused on their battle through the rush-hour traffic that choked the city. When they fell silent it felt uncomfortable.

'Here we are, Ken,' said Lucy. It was just before ten. 'How do you feel?'

'Not too bad,' he replied. He wasn't going to tell her how he really felt – bloody awful. He had visited London many times before but driving through the city this morning the ancient buildings seemed to loom down from the skyline towards him. He felt awkward and out of his depth when normally he felt confident and in control.

'Can I take your ticket, Ken?' A young woman held her hand out towards him. He looked to Lucy, who nodded. He passed it over.

It was at that moment that he realised just how heavy the burden of carrying it around with him the last three days had been. Suddenly he felt calmer – the responsibility now passed to someone else.

'She's going to put it through the machine in the office upstairs,' Lucy explained.

Ken had imagined he would be the one to put it in the machine. That everyone would cheer as it verified the ticket. Instead, they waited for her to return in silence, the only sound coming from the coffee percolator hissing in the corner of the room. Ken felt numb – the same as he had when he first ticked off those six numbers from the newspaper. She returned moments later with a huge grin spread across her face. Ken felt like an observer, uninvolved in what was going on around him as he watched her hand a cheque to Lucy.

Lucy walked towards him. He got to his feet.

'Congratulations, Ken,' she said as she handed him the cheque then shook his hand. 'Enjoy it!'

He looked at his sons one by one, returning their smiles as if in a dream. His heart raced and his breathing quickened as he looked down at the cheque. His stomach churned as he took in what was written on it. The first thing that registered was his name – Kenneth White – typed in black ink. Then he looked at the amount – six million, six hundred thousand pounds. People were talking around him, but while he was aware of their voices he couldn't focus on what they were saying.

He felt someone grasp his hand in theirs and shake it. It was David. Then Stephen did the same, followed by Richard. Julie and Susan kissed him on the cheek. Their touch felt strange – the only thing that seemed real in the room was the cheque he held in his hand.

Lucy looked at her watch. 'OK, everyone, we need to get moving now. The press are waiting to meet you.'

* * *

The cheque was taken away by one of Camelot's bankers, who had already set up accounts in Ken's and his sons' names. Ken had explained he would be giving them a million each, so he was advised to declare the win as a syndicate. Otherwise, if he died within the next seven years, they would have to pay inheritance tax.

He was the first of many financial advisers Ken would be introduced to over the weeks to come. But at that moment Ken had other things on his mind – dealing with the press conference that was now only minutes away.

Before they left the building Lucy asked him if there was anything she or her colleagues could do to help him. Ken was determined to return home with the present he had promised Sheila but was wondering when he would get chance to go out and buy it.

'Would one of your girls get chance to nip out to a jeweller's and get me a locket to take home to Sheila?' he asked. Lucy assured him that wouldn't be a problem.

The splendour of the Waldorf was completely lost on Ken as he walked through the reception area. He looked at his sons. Their faces were ashen, as he was sure his was. He wanted to go home, to start living his life again after three days where it had felt as though it were on hold.

Lucy opened the doors to the room where the press were waiting. He took a deep breath and followed her through them.

She led them on to a platform at the front of the room. They were each shown to a seat with a long table in front of them. The room was full of reporters, photographers and television crews. They all glanced up at the family for a moment and then continued their conversations with the person next to them. He watched them with more interest than they showed him. He had expected the barrage of questions and camera flashes to start the moment they walked into the room. The journalists seemed more interested in chatting among themselves.

'All right?' Lucy mouthed at him. He nodded.

'OK, everyone, I think we're ready to begin.' Her voice sounded different – more forceful than he had ever heard it. 'Ken's happy to answer any of your questions, but try to keep them one at a time, please.'

'How do you feel, Ken?' A camera bulb flashed from the middle of the room.

'Great – I feel great.' He leant into the mass of microphones on the table in front of him. 'We all do.' More flashes from the cameras.

'How will you spend the money?' Ken tried to see where the question had come from but it was impossible to tell. He directed his answer to them all.

'Oh, I decided that a long time ago – a cruise first and when I get back I'll get myself a new Daimler.' Ken grinned at his audience. He was starting to enjoy himself.

One of the journalists waved his notebook in the air to attract his attention. 'Did you ever dream you would win, Ken?'

'Oh, I knew I would. My boys used to take the mickey because I spent so much each week on tickets. Twenty-three pounds a week I pay out – but I nearly always win something.'

The same reporter turned to his sons. 'Did you think he was wasting his money?'

Stephen and Richard stared back – they had already told Ken they wouldn't be answering any questions.

'He's a born optimist, me dad,' said David. 'Each week he would tell us, "Roll on next Saturday for the draw – then I can book myself a cruise to New Zealand on Sunday to see our Auntie Mavis."'

'So it's a case of "I told you so",' piped up another voice from the crowd.

'Oh, yes,' laughed Ken. 'I told them after I'd won that on my gravestone they'll have to put "He did it in the end".'

Ken watched as the journalists scribbled in their notebooks. Every few seconds a camera bulb flashed. The TV cameramen adjusted their lenses, panning across them and focusing in on Ken each time he spoke. It was exciting, exhilarating. He was enjoying every minute of it.

'Will you be buying yourself a mansion, Ken?'

'No, no. We'll be staying put. There would only be me and Sheila rolling around in it. We're happy where we are.'

'Your dad's giving you three sons a million each, isn't he? How do you feel about that?'

David answered for them. 'Well, everything's gone a bit mad, I suppose. It's brilliant what Dad's done for us, but it's thrown everything into chaos. I've worked hard to build my shops up. You work so you can pay your mortgage and live comfortably. This has brought everything forward thirty years.'

'What about you?' called out another reporter, looking directly at Stephen. 'You don't have to work again if you don't want to. What do you do?'

'Well, er . . . yeah. I'm a courier driver. I probably will give that up, but I'll find something else to do.'

'Will it change you, Ken?'

'Nah, not me. I'll still play my darts down the pub, and I'm not going to start drinking champagne instead of bitter or anything. I've had money before, you see – not millions, but enough to be comfortable. And I've lost it too.'

All eyes in the room focused on him. He heard Stephen breathe in sharply. The lads wouldn't like this, but he was going to tell the journalists everything – then they wouldn't be able to drag it up in a few days' time.

'I went bang in the 1980s, you see. Lost everything – my business, my home. It's good to know we'll never have a worry like that again. I've saved up in the past for cruises and the like, but then something's gone wrong for us and I've had to spend it on bailing us out. This time I'm going on my cruise – nothing can stop me now.'

'So you think it'll make you happy?'

'Well, if you can't be happy with £6.6 million you never will be,' Ken laughed.

'What about the rest of you? Will you change?'

'Yes, probably,' said Stephen. 'Of course it will change us – but whether we'll be happy or not we'll just have to wait and see.'

The questions died down.

'Everyone happy then?' asked Lucy.

'Can we just take them outside for some pictures?' called out one of the photographers.

Ken nodded.

On the way out Stephen pulled his father to one side. 'I couldn't believe it when you started telling them about going bang. Why did you do that? You didn't have to – nobody asked.'

'I know that. But what's the point in trying to hide anything? I'm not ashamed of it, and if we give them a good enough story now they'll leave us alone. By the end of the week we'll be old news this way. Trust me.'

They piled out on to the street outside the hotel. The photographers all seemed to want the same picture – the four of them together with an exploding bottle of champagne. They obliged. The whole performance took an hour.

Back at Camelot's offices Lucy asked Ken if there was anywhere they would like to go. 'I'll arrange for you to do some sightseeing. A bit of shopping maybe – spend some of that money.'

'You're all right, love. I think we'll be getting off home soon.'

Ken had already talked it over with his sons. They wanted to start getting back to normal – whatever normal would be from now on.

'Oh, Ken, surely not. There's so much for you to do and see. There's a whole load of chat shows that would love to have you on – they've all been calling asking if they can interview you.'

'Oh, no. We've had enough of all that,' said Ken.

'But, Ken, what's the rush?' Lucy pushed. 'Anyway – I haven't had chance to arrange any cars yet to get you back to Leigh.'

But Ken wasn't going to change his mind. 'That's all right, love,' he said. 'You just call us a couple of cabs to Euston Station and we'll find our own way home.'

'Will you be all right?' she said with concern as she placed her hand on his arm.

'We're big boys now,' laughed Ken. 'I think we can find our way out of the big city by ourselves. What do you think, lads?'

Then Ken remembered Sheila's present. 'You didn't get chance to send out for that trinket for Sheila, did you?'

Lucy reached into her pocket. 'I nearly forgot. Here you are,' she said, handing him a gift-wrapped box in a carrier bag from out of her bag.

'How much do I owe you ?' Ken asked, reaching into his pocket for his wallet. The man from the bank had given him four thousand pounds advance on his cheque to give them some spending money until it cleared.

Lucy looked at the receipt. 'Fifty-four pounds, please.'

Sheila wasn't going to be happy. He'd picked up a cheque for £6.6 million and was returning home with a £54 necklace. Still, they were hardly going to blow a fortune on his behalf.

Lucy held the taxi door open as the driver put the bags in the boot. 'This isn't really goodbye, you know, Ken,' she said. 'We don't just hand over the money and leave you to it. If you have any problems with reporters or anything to do with the money you must call me. We'll look after you in whatever way we can.'

Ken smiled. 'We'll be fine. But if we need help I will ring.'

Lucy looked serious. 'Those reporters wanted to know if the money would change you,' she said quietly. 'It doesn't have to. But what will happen is the people around you will change. For some it will just be temporary – they'll get used to the idea that you're a millionaire and will soon realise you haven't changed as people. Others will never be the same towards you again. That's something you will have to learn to live with.'

As the car pulled away and Lucy went back into the building, David turned to his father. 'Just treat it like another deal, Dad. Only this time it's gone right for all of us. We've got nothing to worry about from now on.'

'You're right, son. Let's just get home, eh? Then we can all get back to normal.'

Ken walked into the house. Sheila had gone to bed. The first thing that struck him was the silence. He had been surrounded by noise and bustle for the last three days. He felt relieved.

He was tired and ready for bed. He crept up the stairs and walked quietly into the bedroom so as not to wake Sheila.

'Ken – is that you?'

'Of course it's me. Who else are you expecting?'

He sat on the bed and leant over to kiss her on the cheek. 'Everything's sorted out now. We can start getting on with it now,' he said.

'The papers have been round again this afternoon. I told them all to come back tomorrow. You'll sort them out then, won't you?'

Ken promised he would. He had expected them to have lost interest by now.

'I'll give them their interviews this week – then that's it. They can't expect any more than that.'

'Can't you just tell them to sod off?' asked Sheila. 'You don't have to talk to them.'

Ken had already turned down Camelot's request for the family to appear on the following Saturday's lottery show at Sheila's insistence. She wasn't going to tell him how to handle the newspaper lot as well.

'I know what I'm doing, Sheila. Just leave it to me.'

He leant down and unzipped his overnight bag. 'I got you that present,' he said as he rummaged among the dirty clothes trying to feel for the carrier bag. Sheila sat up as he passed it to her.

Ken hadn't seen the necklace yet. It had been gift-wrapped before it was handed to him.

Sheila clicked the box open and pulled out the flimsy gold chain. 'Is this it?' she sneered. 'You win the bloody lottery and you come home with this . . . this piece of tat.' She threw it back at him.

Ken laughed. 'I know, love. I know.' He explained what had happened, and Sheila began to laugh too.

'I'll take you shopping in the week – buy you something really special. Did you ask them to deliver all the papers for me tomorrow like I asked?'

'Yes,' grunted Sheila, her smiles vanishing. She obviously wasn't looking forward to seeing them – she hated fuss. Sheila lay back down in the bed and got herself comfortable. The conversation was over.

Ken laid the day's newspapers out on the kitchen table. There were stories about them in every tabloid. He felt strange looking at the photographs of him and the boys grinning back at him. It felt as though much more than a day had passed since they were taken. The stories were all pretty much the same. They all mentioned the bankruptcy and the fact that he would be going off on a cruise and buying a Daimler.

'Here – take a look at this, Sheila,' he said, passing

her a cup of tea. He pointed to a story in the *Sun*. There was a picture of a gravestone with Ken's face superimposed on it and the words HE DID IT IN THE END inscribed underneath. He laughed. 'I like that one,' he said.

'Are they good stories, then?' asked Sheila, peering over his shoulder.

'Oh, yeah – they're fine. They've not put anything I didn't say in.'

Sheila sat down and started to move the papers about so that she could see each story.

'What's this?' she exclaimed, seeing the headline in the *Daily Mail*. 'LOTTERY BANKROLLS AN EX-BANKRUPT FOR SIX MILLION? Oh, Ken – why did you tell them that? People didn't need to know about that.'

'Oh, give over, Sheila. They would have found out. Anyway, I thought our Stephen would have told you all about that.'

'No. I've not spoken to him yet. And what's this about you buying your dream car? You've had Daimlers before. These stories make us sound like we used to be paupers.'

'Give over, Sheila. They've got to sell their papers. They're not doing any harm.'

Sheila stood up. 'You might not care about everybody knowing our business, but I do.'

'Well, you're just going to have to put up with it, Sheila.'

She walked out of the room, slamming the door shut behind her.

Ken started to cut the stories from out of the newspapers. The grandchildren would enjoy looking through them when they were older.

* * *

The rest of the week was spent choosing furniture for the house and arranging for workmen to fit new central heating, windows and doors throughout and a new kitchen and conservatory. Eventually, Ken and Sheila did decide to move from their old terraced house, but in the meantime they filled it with the best that money could buy.

'I've decided we will be going on that lottery show on Saturday,' said Sheila as she looked through some kitchen designs.

'What? I thought you didn't want all that,' said Ken. She had been adamant she wouldn't be involved in any publicity and had refused point-blank to appear on that show when they were first asked.

The telephone rang and Sheila leapt from her seat to answer it. Normally she let it ring until Ken answered, complaining that the call wouldn't be for her anyway.

She returned to the kitchen looking pleased. 'That was Camelot checking about the cars for Saturday. I've told them to send a coach.'

'What are you talking about, Sheila?'

'We'll need a coach to take us to London. We're all going on the show – the grandchildren and everyone. Now David and Lynne are back together there'll be enough of us to fill it.'

'So everyone's going on, then? When was this decided?'

'Oh, just yesterday. That's all right, isn't it?'

'I suppose so,' said Ken. 'I'd better just ring them back – have a chat with them about it.'

'Just leave it to me, Ken,' snapped Sheila. 'I've got it all under control. I'm capable of sorting some things out, you know.'

Ken decided to do just that. She was obviously enjoying making the arrangements, and he did tend to take things over. It seemed to be doing her good – people ringing up wanting to talk to just her.

'You just have yourself ready for when that coach arrives on Saturday morning,' said Sheila. 'I need to make a quick phone call.'

Ken picked up the pile of cards and letters from the doormat. The postman had been delivering dozens each day, and they showed no sign of letting up. Most were from friends and relatives who had heard about the win and wanted to wish them well. Some were from people wanting financial help with various business ventures; others were hard-luck stories hoping for a handout. David had said he would take care of the post from now on, sorting out the begging letters from the genuine well-wishers. Ken normally left them on the hall table for when he called, but today he noticed that one of the envelopes didn't have a stamp. It must have been delivered by hand. He laid it down with the others and began to walk away, but curiosity got the better of him and he turned back to pick it up.

It was from a young couple who lived at the opposite end of the street. At first Ken thought it was a letter congratulating them on their win.

You must be feeling very pleased with yourselves . . ., he read. *It must be wonderful not to have to worry about money any more.*

Then, as he read on, he began to frown.

What do you think you're doing staying round here with all that money in the bank? How do you think people like us are going to feel seeing

millionaires coming and going? We don't know how
we're going to pay our mortgage from one month to
the next while you can afford a mansion somewhere.
Just clear off and live with the other millionaires and
leave us to get on with being poor.

Ken threw the letter down. That wasn't fair; he
didn't deserve any of that, he thought. He had every
right to live there. OK, so some of his neighbours had
money problems. But surely that didn't mean he had
to move away from the place he had put down roots
in?

For a moment he wondered if he should offer the
couple some money to help them through their bad
patch. He quickly decided against it. They didn't
want his help; their sole intention in writing that
letter was to hurt him.

That would be the last personal letter Ken would
open himself. From then on, he vowed he would
leave all that to David.

Ken wondered if the couple would be joining him
in the Foundry that night, where he had arranged a
free bar to celebrate his win. He hoped not – he
didn't want anything to spoil the party.

Ken had been a regular at the Foundry every
Thursday night for as long as he could remember.
Walking the four hundred yards from his home to
the pub was part of his weekly routine. It was
something he always did with Richard – he didn't
have to think about it.

Only tonight was different. Tonight he would be
the centre of attention. He thought back to Lucy's
warning that it would be the people around him who
would change even if he stayed the same.

'All right, Dad?' Richard asked as they reached the door. Ken nodded. He was about to find out if she was right.

The pub was heaving as he made his way to the bar. People slapped him on the back and offered him their hands to shake. He hadn't needed to be nervous after all. He looked over at the group of drinkers near the dartboard where he normally played each Monday night as a member of the pub team. The captain, Ernie Bowen, pointed towards the board and grinned. There was a picture of Ken from out of the newspaper pinned to it. A couple of darts were sticking out of his nose. Ken roared with laughter.

'You'd better be in for Monday's match,' Ernie called over. 'Your name's on the team-sheet, so I'll have to fine you if you're not. I don't care if you're a millionaire!'

'Oh, I'll be there,' laughed Ken.

He noticed that some of the newspaper reporters and photographers had turned up to share a drink with him. He raised his pint glass in their direction. There was no sign of the couple who had sent the letter. He was glad. The only comments he was getting from people in the pub were positive.

'Will it change you, Ken?' he was asked for the tenth time that evening, this time by someone he didn't even recognise.

'Oh, no, I don't think so,' he replied as though he had never been asked the question before.

As he stood in his usual spot, watching his friends and people who just happened to have called in the pub that evening enjoying their free drinks, he felt happier than he had all week. He had expected people to take advantage – drinking shorts or champagne all night – but everyone was on their usual pints. Not that he would have minded, he thought to himself, but it was good to see.

He walked home that evening certain he would never have to deal with any resentment from the people around him – not if that night was anything to go by, anyway.

'You can drop us off at the hotel, mate,' Ken told the coach driver as they approached London. 'I don't want to be going straight to the BBC.'

'Sorry, sir. I've been told I have to take you straight to the studios.'

'Never mind that,' Ken argued. 'I want a bit of a rest first.'

'Leave it, Ken,' interrupted Sheila. 'Let him follow his orders.'

The rest of the family agreed with Sheila. He decided to let it go.

At the studios Ken and his sons were shown to one dressing room to change and Sheila and the wives and grandchildren to another. Minutes later Julie hammered on the door calling for Ken to come out.

'Ken – it's Sheila. She's got herself into a bit of a state. You'd better come.'

In the other room Sheila was sat on a chair in the corner fanning herself with a magazine. She was panting and obviously distressed.

'What is it, love? What's wrong?'

'Have you seen the size of this room? There's all of us and they expect us all to get changed in here. It's disgusting – they're treating us like animals.'

The room was very small and with so many people inside it was getting hot and stuffy.

'I'm not going on now, Ken. No way am I going on their bloody show.'

'Oh, now, Sheila, love. You've come all this way –'

'Ken – leave it. I'm not going on. They have to know they can't treat people like this.'

Ken knew he had to accept her decision. He had been amazed she had agreed to go on the show in the first place and had been thrilled to have her with them on the coach. Deep down he had suspected she would find a reason not to go on and this was it. If it hadn't been the dressing room it would have been something else.

'All right, love, all right. You stay there and I'll fetch you a glass of water. Nobody's going to make you do anything you're not happy with.'

Ken sat at the front of the audience waiting for the cameras to start rolling. Richard was to his right and to his left an empty seat.

Anthea Turner, the lottery show's anchorwoman, was cracking jokes with the audience about stories in the newspapers about her quitting. The empty seat was for her.

'You don't believe what you read in the newspapers, do you?' she asked them. 'Unless it's something nice – you'll believe that.' The audience laughed. They seemed to like her.

Ken had met her before the show and instantly took to her. She was easy to talk to and not at all affected in the way the papers made her out to be. He wished he had agreed to a request from GMTV for him to be interviewed by her earlier in the week.

The titles began to roll and Ken's heart pounded. It was one thing talking to reporters for newspaper stories that would be printed the following day, another altogether talking to Anthea Turner live on national television.

Someone on the studio floor began to wave his arms at the audience and made a clapping motion. Everyone began to cheer and applaud the way they had been shown in rehearsals.

Anthea began waving and started to welcome the viewers to the show. Ken was oblivious to what she was saying. He was just waiting for the moment she would be seated next to him.

A tape was being played out to the people watching at home. It was giving ideas for what people could spend their money on if they won the lottery. When this finished Ken knew, from the rehearsal, that that would be Anthea's cue to introduce him. He breathed deeply. Anthea came and took her place. She grabbed hold of his hand and gave it a squeeze.

'All right?' she mouthed at him, smiling warmly. He nodded back.

A man behind the camera pointing at him started to count her in. 'Five, four . . .' he said, counting down on his fingers. He stayed silent for the three, two, one.

'Well, sitting here next to me is Ken White from Manchester. Now, he could buy the palace if he wanted to,' she said, referring to one of the houses for sale in the previous film.

Ken stared into the camera. He could read the words he was hearing on the inside of its lens. Anthea had explained earlier that this was called autocue. He was entranced by it.

'Now he has won £6.6 million.'

The audience began to whoop, and Ken felt a broad smile spread across his face.

Anthea thrust a microphone towards him. 'Well, Ken, I don't think I've sat so close to somebody who's won so much money,' she teased. 'How does it feel?'

'Oh, great. Fantastic.' The audience burst into laughter. Ken laughed too as he realised what an understatement he was making.

She asked him to introduce to the viewers his family, who were in seats behind and next to him. Then she wanted to know what plans he had for the money.

'We're going to go on a cruise to New Zealand –'

'Oh, lovely,' she interrupted. 'Now, why New Zealand?'

'To see my sister. Haven't been over since 1986, so that's the last time I saw her.'

Anthea nodded her head in encouragement. She looked pleased. He felt more confident now.

'What's her name?'

'Mavis,' Ken replied.

'I know that you haven't seen Mavis since 1986,' said Anthea. 'And, er, I know that you're a very close family as well, aren't you? And she's actually very sad that she can't be with you tonight to share this momentous occasion in your life.' Then she paused and looked at the ground. 'Well, actually, no, I'm fibbing there. It's not quite true. Because Mavis wanted to be with you so much tonight, and the rest of the family, that she has travelled twelve thousand miles to be with you tonight.'

The noise of a drum roll filled the studio. They hadn't rehearsed this bit.

'Ladies and gentlemen, would you please welcome Mavis, Ken's sister.'

The audience began to cheer and clap. Ken felt tears prick his eyes as he realised what she was saying. His beloved little sister was about to be in the same room as him for the first time in years.

Two giant doors on the stage on the studio floor in front on him slowly parted, and there stood Mavis with her husband, a huge grin fixed on her face.

He started to move towards them but Anthea placed her arm over his. 'You stay here,' she said. He only just heard her over the noise of the crowd.

'Hello, love,' said Ken, flinging his arms around her and squeezing her tightly. He didn't have time to think about the fact he was sharing such an emotional moment with so many people. So this was why Sheila had suddenly changed her mind about coming here. And Mavis must have been at the hotel when he asked the driver to take them there. Sheila had been helping the BBC spring this surprise on him.

Mavis took the empty seat and they clutched each other's hands as they watched the draw take place. This wasn't the time or place to talk. They could do that later. Instead, they just kept turning to look at each other and grin.

As the closing titles rolled, Ken realised that his week in the limelight was over. There would be new winners tonight who would take his place. Ken White and his family were old news. The last seven days felt like a rite of passage. Now, the time had finally come for them to start living their new life.

Chapter Four

DAVID WHITE AND HIS WIFE LYNNE sat together at the kitchen table. Their daughters, Helena and Kate, had already gone to bed, exhausted after the excitement of the trip to London and appearing on television.

'This is it, Lynne – a new start for all of us.'

Lynne nodded and smiled. David took hold of her hand and squeezed it tightly. There had been moments in the last few days when he had wondered if he would ever be part of a family scene like this again.

The Monday before his dad won the lottery, David had been at work in his electrical shop when he had taken a call from his eldest daughter's headmistress. She had wanted to know where fifteen-year-old Helena was.

'Why are you asking me?' David had asked her. 'In one of your classrooms, I should think.'

But Helena had been missing classes for weeks now, and her teachers suspected that the notes she brought in explaining her absence were forged.

Back at home David discovered that Lynne had known all about their daughter's truancy.

'Why the hell didn't you tell me?' David yelled at her.

'Because I thought I'd be able to sort it out without having to worry you.'

'Christ Almighty, Lynne. I'm her father. I should have been given the chance to help sort this out.'

He turned to Helena. 'And you – how many times have I told you how bloody important a good education is? Do you want to end up working on a checkout somewhere, relying on some creep who treats you badly to keep you?'

'I won't,' said Helena through gritted teeth.

'Oh, won't you? You know better, do you? Well, listen to me. Men treat women badly – I should know, I'm one. But uneducated women – they walk all over them. I want you to be able to walk out of any bad relationship and stand on your own feet. How will you do that without your exams behind you?'

'I know, Dad, I know. I'll stop it – I promise I will.'

'You're a bright girl. You can sail through your exams if you put the work in. Christ, when I think how I struggled at school – you've got it easy.'

David had skipped plenty of classes himself as a schoolboy. Throughout his childhood no one ever picked up on the fact that he was dyslexic. He was never offered any help and instead was put into classes for the slow learners. He hated being made to feel like he was stupid and so would refuse to go.

He remembered how he had felt then, his confidence battered every time he tried to read off the blackboard. He understood everything he heard but found it impossible to put any of it down on paper.

'Do you want Social Services knocking on the door

threatening to take us to court, the way they did with my parents?'

'Leave her alone, Dave,' Lynne interrupted. 'She's said she won't do it any more.'

Lynne was fiercely protective of her girls even with David. He hated the way they seemed to shut him out.

'How many times has she told you that, eh? How many times have you let her get away with this? Were you ever going to tell me?'

He looked at Helena again. 'I used to get a pasting off me dad for not going to school, but I was so bloody miserable I'd rather that than have to go.' He paced around the room. 'What's your excuse? You just don't bloody feel like it. You're going through a rebellious phase. For Christ's sake, Helena –'

Helena began to cry, and Lynne put her arms around her to comfort her.

'Oh, great. So this is all my fault again, is it? Can someone please tell me how this is my fault?'

David went to the bedroom and packed a bag. He had to get away.

Lynne pulled her hand free and leant back into her chair. 'I must have been the last person in town to know your dad had won.'

She had called him a liar when he had gone to the house to tell her about the money.

'That Monday I sat there counting out coppers to see how much money I had so that I didn't have to ask you for any. I even asked next door if they could wait until I picked up my Family Allowance to pay the rent for the stables.'

The family lived in an old farmhouse with stables

alongside which they rented off their neighbours. Lynne and the girls kept horses there.

'I told them that you'd been trying to con me into thinking you'd won the lottery so I'd talk to you. They probably knew you had by then and thought I was completely mad.'

David laughed. 'No change there, then!' Then he looked serious. 'Look, Lynne. I don't want them thinking this money means they can give up on school, that it doesn't matter any more. It *does* matter.'

'I know that.'

'Well, just make sure they do.'

He left it at that. There had been enough fighting between them, and he saw no sense in reopening old wounds. He was just glad to be back with his family again.

He thought back to the night he spent in the hotel in London before they picked up the cheque. He had felt so miserable and alone. Lynne was still refusing to speak to him, and he had no idea what the future had in store. He had toyed with the idea of leaving for good. With a million pounds in the bank he could have had some serious fun.

But however appealing that might have been, it was never an option. He and Lynne had been together almost twenty years. They'd met when he was just eighteen and she was twenty-one and had married seven months later. He had had enough of hanging out at nightclubs even then and knew he wanted a more solid base for his life. Once the girls were born he firmly believed that his sole purpose in life was to provide for them and strive to give them the best. If he walked out on them now, he would be going against everything he believed in.

They were both silent, Lynne clearly lost in her thoughts about what the future held for them all. David found the quiet comforting. There were so few people in his life that he felt close enough to for a break in the conversation not to be uncomfortable. He watched her face and wondered what she was thinking. He hoped this money would boost her confidence. She was very insecure at times – always putting herself down and questioning how much he loved her.

He'd treated her badly at times – he knew that. He was probably to blame in part for her insecurity, throwing her weaknesses back at her to win fights that had turned nasty. But didn't everyone do that?

He wished he hadn't walked out after the argument over Helena. Kate had phoned him a couple of days later in tears and asked him to go back. However cross his children made him at times, he couldn't bear to think of them being hurt – physically or emotionally. But they *did* get hurt when he and Lynne rowed. They both knew that, but still they did it. Usually they fought over money, but that wasn't ever going to be a problem again. David hoped they wouldn't find new battles now that one was over.

He wished Lynne could know, without his having to spell it out, just how in awe of her he felt at times, how much he loved her. He'd never been very good at communicating the emotional stuff, but surely she knew how he felt?

She had dedicated her life to his children, and he knew of no one who could make a better mother than Lynne. He remembered when, as toddlers, the girls had been sick with whooping cough. She had nursed them round the clock, showing them nothing but love and patience. He had never known anyone as patient as Lynne.

There had been periods in the last twenty years when they seemed to row constantly and perhaps would have been better apart. But they had always pulled together again in time to save their marriage.

His own parents' marriage, from what he had seen as he grew up, was very similar. He had witnessed fights between them which culminated in them throwing ornaments at each other. He could remember incidents where they chased each other around the house hurling abuse. He just couldn't remember why.

David thought back to his childhood. His heart sank as he remembered the signs that meant things were going to be bad for a while. For months everything would be normal, then he would return home from school to find his mum just getting out of bed. That would be the start of a period when she would sleep all day and read all night. It was his cue to ask his grandparents if he could stay with them for a while.

He didn't remember dwelling too much on why she did that. He was very independent and was too busy with his boy-scouting and fishing with his friends to fret about it. As an adult he guessed that she suffered from depression. The tablets she took even now were probably antidepressants. It wasn't something they discussed, then or now.

'First thing we've got to do is find somewhere to live,' said David, finally breaking the silence. 'We need a bigger place.'

Lynne nodded. 'I'll get on to the estate agents and we'll have a look at what's about.'

She yawned and looked at the clock. It was only ten but it felt much later.

David grinned at her. 'Come on, you. Let's get an early night. '

David stood up, scraping his chair back behind him. 'Well, what are you waiting for? Get up those stairs before I run off with some leggy twenty-year-old.'

Lynne's face crumpled. He thought she might cry.

'Hey, hey, I'm only joking,' he said, putting his arms around her.

'But it could happen. You'll have women throwing themselves at you now you've got all that money.'

'Who am I with now, Lynne? You. If I'd wanted to run around with other women I wouldn't have come home, would I? Come on, love, let's go to bed.'

Walking into the cooker shop for the first time since the win felt strangely normal. It was like going back to work after a long holiday – that feeling that you have never been away. The pleasantries over with – he hadn't seen some of his staff since before the win – he set to work on the shop floor, looking out for customers who might want some help. He spotted an old lady looking at one of the cookers. He glanced around and saw that all his staff were busy, so he walked over to her and offered his services.

'Are you interested in this model?' he asked her. She looked up at him and then back to the cooker in front of them.

'How much discount will you give me?' she asked him, staring him in the face.

'Oh, I'll let you have it for two-eighty.' The price tag on it was for three hundred pounds.

'All you're going to give me is twenty pounds off this cooker.' She looked around her, checking to see who was watching. Aware that she had an audience, she raised her voice.

'All the money you've got and I'm a pensioner and you're going to charge me two hundred and eighty quid for this cooker?'

'Listen, love – it's my job. I can't give them away.'

'It's disgusting. You should be ashamed of yourself.' The old lady turned and walked out of the shop. David hurried into the office.

He had always expected some level of resentment, but this took him by surprise. It had been so unexpected.

There would have been people in that shop, watching the performance, who would have thought he should have driven round to that old lady's house and given her the cooker for nothing. He doubted they would have felt the same if he had inherited his money and just happened to own a cooker shop. After all, no one asked the director of British Telecom for free phone calls simply because he was loaded.

When his father told him that he would be giving each of his sons a million pounds to spend as they chose David had been shocked. It had thrown his life into turmoil. He had spent his adulthood working hard seven days a week to earn money. Money had been his goal – the fear of not having any driving him on.

Now he had money. More than he, at that moment anyway, knew what to do with. His goal had gone.

He couldn't even come to work any more. His own face was a liability. He had to find a new challenge – something other than money to strive for.

This was David's second insight into the burden of sudden, unexpected wealth. Less than a week after the win he had tried to claw back some normality in his life by keeping to his regular Friday-night squash game. He had barely missed a game with Mike, a former colleague, in fifteen years. Both men were hugely competitive and hauled themselves off the court at the end of the session exhausted. David would be dripping with sweat, his heart pounding and his head spinning.

But this time was different. His thoughts when he walked on to the court were not how many points he intended to win by. He was too busy fretting about what the chances were of his keeling over from a heart attack if he exerted himself too much. He kept thinking about how he had just been given the chance of a lifetime and that the last thing he should be doing was risking his neck. So instead of pushing himself to the limits he missed balls on purpose. The adrenalin rush he used to revel in now frightened him.

He would later turn down flying trips with another old pal for the same reason. The thrill of danger had gone, and it would take months for him to realise that if he didn't take the odd chance there wasn't much point in his being alive.

David stood at the window in the bedroom and stared out across the fields. They still hadn't found anywhere to live, but there was no rush. He liked this house – it had been their home for more than ten years now.

He and Lynne had looked at houses which cost up to a quarter of a million pounds but none of them seemed worth that kind of money. It was crazy the way your perspective on things like that changed. Before he had the money David would look at a house like the ones he had viewed and imagine buying it if only he had the money. Now he had the cash he wanted good value, which he didn't think they were. They were in decent enough areas, but the rooms and gardens were much smaller than he expected. Also, they didn't seem to have any character, or what character they did have was down to the architect who designed them. Maybe that was the answer – to have a house built to his own specifications.

In the distance David could just see the roof of the old farmhouse on the other side of the village. Three years earlier he had knocked on the farmhouse door and asked the owner to let him know if he ever thought about selling. It had never been anything more than a pipe dream. The farm was run down but even so would have been worth far more than he would have got for their house. Even if he had been able to buy it, he wouldn't have had the money or time to take on such a huge project.

'That's it!' David said out loud. For weeks they had been trailing around houses looking for their dream home. Every evening he had stared out of this window across the fields hoping for some inspiration, and all the time the answer had been in his sights. He could afford to buy the farmhouse now and turn that into their home. All he had to do was to convince the old guy who owned it to sell.

* * *

David stood in front of the crumbling building. It was rotting away where it stood through years of neglect, but he barely noticed that. He was too busy trying to envisage what it would look like once he rebuilt it.

He hammered on the back door and prepared to wait for it to open. He seemed to remember the man he spoke to wasn't too steady on his feet. If he was still living there it would take him a while to get to the door.

The door creaked open and the old man peered out from behind it. He smiled at David as though he recognised him.

'Hello, Mr Colshawe. You might not remember me –'

'Oh, I've been waiting for you,' he said. 'I think you'd better come in.'

David laughed. 'You know what I want, then?'

'Aye, I think I do. Come in, lad. I'll make us a brew and then we can talk.'

The chair creaked as David sat down. The table was marked from years of use. He felt as if he had stepped back fifty years as he looked around the old kitchen. The walls were damp and what wallpaper was left was peeling away. Cupboard doors were hanging off the hinges. It was June, yet the air inside seemed colder than when he had stood outside waiting to be let in.

'Are you all right here on your own? Don't you have family who can look after you?' The old man was in his late seventies and less stable on his feet than he remembered. He wheezed as he moved across the kitchen. There was no source of heating that David could see. He doubted he would survive another winter there.

'They'd like to. We don't need anyone to look after us. We look after ourselves.'

He carefully carried a tray over to where David sat. On it were two mugs of steaming hot tea, a sugar bowl and a spoon. David picked up the teaspoon – it gleamed. It was then that he noticed that the place might have been run down but the things in were spotlessly clean. The old couple clearly could look after themselves.

'So, come on, lad. You want to buy this place off me, don't you? Make me an offer.'

'Well, why don't you tell me what you think it's worth first,' said David. 'Tell me how much you're after.'

'Oh, well, it's going to take some persuading to get my wife out. She won't want to leave.'

'How much, then?'

'Well, lad. How badly do you want it? A man who wanted it badly enough would pay big money for this place.'

The negotiations lasted a week. David had asked the old man to get one of his children to join them many times during their meetings. While it was clear to David that Mr Colshawe was perfectly capable of getting a fair price for the farmhouse and land surrounding it, he knew anyone who hadn't been there might think he had taken advantage of him. David had previously run a house-clearance firm and always made sure he never dealt with old people without a witness for that very reason. But Mr Colshawe refused.

Their haggling took place in the gloomy old kitchen or as they walked together across the fields David also wanted to buy. All the time David imagined the place as it could be with his money ploughed into it.

Lynne would be thrilled finally to have stables of her own. There was even a pond in one of the fields which he would be able to stock and have as his own private fishing haven.

They finally agreed on a price and David moved an old caravan on to the land at the side of the building. He would live there and guard the property while the work took place. Lynne and the girls would stay in the old house.

The day the old couple moved out David went to see them off and wish them well.

'Good luck with it, son,' said Mr Colshawe, grasping David by the hand. David felt sad as he saw the suppressed emotion on his face as Mr Colshawe walked out of his kitchen for the last time. He had grown fond of the old guy and got the impression that the feeling was mutual. He was a canny old bloke, and David had stopped seeing him as a frail pensioner but as a shrewd businessman. Now the deal was sealed he looked weak and feeble – far more so than he ever had when they first met.

'Come back and see it, won't you?' David urged him.

Mr Colshawe nodded. As they let go of each other's hand David felt a piece of paper in his palm. It was a grubby old five-pound note.

'What's this?' he asked.

'Just an old Gypsy custom, son. I hope you and your family are happy here.'

* * *

David walked back into the kitchen. He had done it – the first of his dreams was going to be realised. He turned full circle, taking in every wall and imagining how it once might have looked and how it would look months from then.

He had no idea at that point what other dreams he had to make real. All he was interested in was rolling up his sleeves and getting his hands dirty. He didn't simply want to design their new home; he wanted to help build it too. He could stop worrying about what kind of business to go into for a while – this project was going to keep him busy for months.

'I took Kate shopping today for some new clothes,' said Lynne. They had just finished their evening meal and the girls were doing their homework in their rooms.

'Did you get some nice things?' asked David.

The designs for the new kitchen were laid out on the table.

'You'll never guess what she said to me in the shop. She'd chosen what she wanted and then saw another dress and was wondering what she should put back so that she could have it. I told her she could have it as well as the other things and she started laughing. She said "Isn't it great now we're rich, Mum." She was so pleased.'

It was such an innocent comment and said without greed or arrogance. David felt proud. He had been concerned that the girls would think they would get an easy ride now they had so much money. He was determined that wouldn't happen. He still wanted them to do well at school and to find careers of their own. The money would come to them eventually, but he wanted them to appreciate its full value by the time it did.

Lynne went into the living room and switched on the television.

'David, come and see this,' she called. 'There's been a woman murdered on the other side of the village.' She had the local news on. David went through to watch with her.

'It's only up the road, Dave. Christ, it could have been one of us.'

David was staying in the caravan next to the farmhouse and was living between there and with Lynne and the girls at the old house. This made her nervous.

'Give over, love. He would never have got past the Rottweilers.'

'Oh, Dave. I don't know if we should be here on our own.'

The murdered woman was a respectable mother living alone with her young son. She had been raped then murdered in her own home just a couple of miles away.

'Nothing like that's going to happen to you, love. You're well protected by the dogs and I'm not far away.'

Two days later David's mobile rang. He had just taken a delivery of a load of bricks and was about to move them ready for the builders. It was Lynne. 'Dave, the police are on their way. They want to talk to you.'

'Do you know what it's about?' David asked her.

'Something to do with a car parked outside our house. I think they're traffic police.'

A car pulled up outside his caravan and two men

stepped out and started to walk towards him. David guessed they were plain-clothes officers.

'Have you got a minute, Mr White?' one of them called over.

David had had plenty of run-ins with traffic police before and hadn't much time for them. 'Oh, piss off,' he called back. 'If you've come about some petty traffic offence you can fuck off and find somebody else to mither.' He turned his back and began to walk away from them.

'Woah, hang on,' the same officer called back. 'If you'll let me explain. There's been a murder.'

David turned back to face them. They explained that they needed to talk to him in connection with a car that had been seen outside his house. It had also been seen outside the house of the woman whose murder had been reported on the local news.

David told them what he knew about the vehicle and they left. They contacted him later that day to tell him the car had been ruled out of the enquiry.

That night David was in the caravan struggling to sleep. He couldn't stop thinking about the dead woman and the fact that Lynne and the girls were alone while her killer was still out there. He reached down beside the bed for his mobile phone and rang Lynne. She sounded sleepy.

'Oh, great,' he said jokingly, trying to hide the relief he felt on hearing her voice. 'I'm here worrying about you and you're fast asleep.'

The visit from the police had shaken him up. Until then it hadn't seemed such a big deal, that woman dying. But suddenly it felt very close to home.

'Just go and double-check you've locked the doors, will you, love.'

They had been locked and bolted all evening. David lay back in the bed. The sooner this house was finished the better.

Three days later the two police officers returned. David had spent the morning helping build boundary fences on his land. He was heading back to his caravan for a hot drink.

'Oh, Mr White. Hello again. We've got a few questions for you. Can you spare us a few minutes?'

'Yeah, sure,' said David. 'What do you want to know?'

'I think it might be better if we go inside,' said one of them, gesturing towards the caravan.

Inside, David moved a pile of clothes off one of the benches for them to sit down. He perched on the end of the bed. 'What's this about, then?' he asked. Something in their manner made him nervous. They were formal and polite, yet they had been pretty friendly on their last visit. They needed to know where he was on the night the woman was murdered.

'I was here,' said David. His heart began to race as he realised they were going to ask him if he could prove that. He had been alone all night. He remembered it clearly. There had been a dreadful storm and he had wondered if he should get out and drive home in case a tree crashed down on him. He wished he had – then he would have had an alibi.

'On your own?'

David nodded.

'Why are you living in a caravan on your own, anyway? From what we've heard you could afford something a bit better than this.'

'I need to be here to guard the building site.

Otherwise I'll have some scallies breaking in and wrecking the place.'

'We need to get a statement off you – just to help us with the enquiry. Do you object to that?'

'No, not at all.'

One of the officers, Steve Ford, picked a case up off the floor and opened it. 'We need to take some blood off you as well for DNA. It's in your own interest. Once we've got the results we can rule you out.'

That night David couldn't sleep. He knew he hadn't had anything to do with the woman's death, yet he was having to prove it. The police obviously thought he was a serious suspect because of the way he was living.

On the one hand he was glad to have given the DNA sample; that would rule him out immediately. But on the other he couldn't stop thinking that mistakes could be made. You were always hearing about miscarriages of justice – people being sent to prison for crimes they just didn't commit.

It took two weeks for the results to come back. Throughout that time David was worried sick. He kept waiting for the police to return. Every car that pulled up made him jump as he wondered if it was them.

Lynne was frightened too. Not because she feared for his liberty – she never even asked him if he had been involved – but because the killer was still at large, and the way she saw it the police were wasting time talking to her husband.

David knew from the smile on Steve Ford's face as he opened the caravan door that he was in the clear. But it wasn't all good news.

'Listen, mate, I'm sorry about this but we need to speak to your brothers now,' he said.

'You what? Why do you need to speak to them?'

'We just do. Can you put us in touch?'

'This is crazy,' said David. 'I can understand you taking statements and samples from me because I'm local and I'm living on my own here. But my brothers – they don't even live in the village.'

'Look, we need to talk to them and get blood off them to rule them out as well.'

By now David had struck up a relationship with the policemen and he pushed Steve to tell him why. He refused. David reluctantly agreed to contact Richard and Stephen so they could also be interviewed.

Their tests also came back negative after a fortnight of sleepless nights for them and their families.

Despite his anger towards the police for what he saw as a waste of time and money, David made them welcome at his caravan throughout the six-month murder investigation. They would call in for a drink and a chat every Friday afternoon after their weekly briefings at the incident room in the village. David would make it clear to them that he believed he and his brothers had become suspects because of their high profile locally through the lottery win.

'Some jealous copper put our names into the frame, didn't he?' he would accuse them. But they refused to discuss the case with him any further.

Then at six o'clock one morning he heard a pair of knuckles rapping against his caravan window. He opened the curtain to see Steve Ford grinning back at him.

'We've got him,' he mouthed, making a thumbs-up sign before turning and walking back to his car where one of his colleagues was waiting with the engine running.

'Thank God,' thought David.

A couple of weeks later Steve returned to visit David. 'Listen, mate. I do some charity work and I wondered if you fancied helping out.'

David tried to hide his disappointment. In recent months, since the win, his circle of friends had decreased and he felt close to few people outside his immediate family. He had begun to confide in Steve about how this affected him. People who had once been close to him didn't seem to want to know any more. David could rationalise why this was happening – the last thing they would want to see as they struggled to meet their mortgage payments was a guy with a big smile, building a big house with hundreds of thousands of pounds sitting in the bank. He could sympathise – but it didn't stop it hurting. He got the impression that the friends who now stayed away would rather not see the trappings of his million pounds. That way they didn't feel let down by what they had. David thought Steve had come to call on him as a friend – but instead he just wanted a donation to some police charity.

'How much are you after?' David asked, opening the drawer where he kept his chequebook.

'I'm not after your money, mate. It's your time I want.'

Steve ran murder-mystery events and wanted David to help out. David was thrilled to be asked – it confirmed his hopes that his relationship with Steve had nothing to do with his money. On the night, they raised more than five hundred pounds. David got more pleasure from giving his time to help raise that money than he ever would have from handing over a cheque for the same amount. It made him feel like Steve respected him.

A few months later Steve would retire from the force and become David's right-hand man, helping him run the various businesses he eventually invested in and providing a solid sounding board on whatever problems were to come.

The house completed, David and his family moved in.

His project over, David went out for a drink with Steve Ford. Steve had watched the house being built during his weekly visits through the murder enquiry. It seemed appropriate to celebrate with him. He returned home in the early hours expecting Lynne to be in bed. The girls were staying with friends.

He tiptoed up the stairs, anxious not to wake her. But as he glanced up he saw Lynne at the top, wearing full make-up and a tight-fitting dress, her hands placed firmly on her hips.

'Lynne?' He was confused.

'What's wrong, Dave? Can't you manage another shag tonight?'

'What the fuck are you talking about? You're not making bloody sense, woman.'

'I know where you've been. I know what you've been doing. Any good, was she?'

'You're mad,' said David, turning round and going back down the stairs.

Lynne charged down after him. 'I got a phone call.

"The lottery winner's out having fun," she said. She told me your car was parked outside some woman's house and that you were inside giving her the time of her life.'

She took off one of her shoes and hurled it down the stairs after him.

'Well, you bastard. Who was she? Good, was she – better than me? Thinner than me?' She began to weep, lowering herself, exhausted, on to one of the stairs. 'You promised you wouldn't do this to me. You promised.'

David felt desperately sorry for her. She looked so unhappy, so shattered. He climbed back up to where she sat and placed himself next to her. 'Lynne – think about it. We've just moved into a bloody great house and we've got more money than most people round here will ever see. Some jealous bitch has just tried to cause us some trouble. I've been out with Steve – nobody else.'

'Promise me you're not lying, Dave. I'll never forgive you if you do anything like that.'

'You've got to trust me, Lynne. You've nothing to worry about.'

Now his house was finished and he couldn't risk showing his face in his shops any more, David knew it was time to find a new business to run. He needed something else to drive him on.

A transport firm Richard had worked for in the past was in financial difficulties and had approached the family for help. After a long period of consultation they agreed to do that – but instead of handing cash over to bail them out they instead bought the company outright. Turning it around would be David's next challenge.

He returned to work with renewed vigour, but for the first time in his life also felt able to enjoy some time at home with his family. All his life he had worked seven days a week to attain money and possessions. He had always been certain he would become wealthy through hard work and determination. The lottery had made him richer than he ever imagined, literally overnight. Now he had everything he had ever aspired to own, he realised that, corny as it might seem, happiness was his greatest asset. Time with his family and time to himself were more valuable than the expensive cars in his drive and the extravagant objects he could afford to buy without thinking.

He had had to rethink his whole attitude towards possessions. One moment towards the end of the first summer in their new home brought this home to him. He was sat in his boat on his pond, the sun beating down on him. As he gazed contentedly over his land, the house he had always dreamt of owning looming in the background, he suddenly realised that he was really only the caretaker of it all. One day he would leave and someone else would live here.

He had strived for these possessions for so long, yet now he had them he didn't feel different or better in any way. He was content, but now it was all his he knew he could have been happy without any of it. Yet that was something he would never have known if he hadn't had these things in the first place.

He wandered back towards the house. As he entered the kitchen the telephone was ringing. It was Julie – she was crying.

'Calm down, Julie, calm down and tell me what's happened.'

He listened to what she had to say and then slowly replaced the receiver.

Richard had been arrested on suspicion of illegally importing cannabis. The house and his offices had been searched and Richard taken in for questioning.

David paced around the kitchen as what she had told him sunk in. Richard had been living like some kind of playboy ever since the win, and David had expressed his concerns many times about the people he was hanging out with. He didn't doubt that these drinking friends of his brother's were involved. 'Stupid, stupid little shit,' he said aloud to himself, sitting down at the table before slamming his fist down on it in frustration. 'Why didn't he fucking listen to me?'

He thought back to a conversation he had had with his brothers and his father on the train back from London the day they'd received the cheque. He had warned them then that the millions they had just collected wouldn't necessarily bring them all happiness – it could just as easily lead to their downfall.

His only insight into the effect that great wealth could have on a family was the episodes of the US soap *Dallas* he had watched as he grew up. He had always been fascinated by the way the family the series revolved around, the Ewings, was permanently at war over the money they were too busy fighting over to enjoy.

'We've got to be honest with each other,' he had told them. 'Nothing hidden and no secrets. We've got to stick together from now on.'

The following morning the story of Richard's arrest would make the front page of the *Sun*. That day there were no customers at either of David's shops, and there never would be again. Rumours spread that it wasn't just Richard but the whole family who was in trouble with the police over drugs. Eventually David would be forced to close down his shops as it became clear that local opinion was set firmly against them all. They had gone from being famous to notorious.

In the months that followed, David discovered he had breached various planning regulations when he built the house and would eventually be forced to demolish part of it to satisfy the local council. Again, this was reported by the media. Any ideas he had that the lottery money would see the end of problems for his family were naive in the extreme. Their problems had merely just started.

Chapter Five

RICHARD WHITE SLOWLY PEERED OUT from behind his hands and forced himself to take in the police holding cell where he had just spent half the night. There was a toilet, with no seat, in the corner opposite the solid wooden bench where he had lain for hours. The cell, about twelve by eight feet, smelt stale. A dim red light had been on all night, but he had kept his eyes closed as he tried to fathom what was happening to him. Now daylight made it softer – but that couldn't alter the harshness of his surroundings. The discoloured cream walls were covered in graffiti, some etched with cigarette lighters, others scratched on with fingernails. JIM WAS ERE 1996. MUFC. The room hadn't seen a paintbrush in years.

He threw the grey blanket off his legs and sat up, leaning forward into his hands. His mouth felt dirty, as did his whole body. His neck was stiff and his back ached – there had been no pillow to rest on.

Richard felt more bewildered than frightened. He had no idea why he was there. He was charged with conspiring to import illegal substances, but he didn't know why. He just wanted to be able to make some sense of what was happening to him. His confusion hadn't been helped by the constant switching on and off of the brighter cell light that took over from the dim red throughout the night. That had destroyed any chance of sleep.

Richard looked to the window – it was covered in bars and too high to look through. He just wanted the questions to start so that he could answer them and go home. He had done nothing wrong. Christ – he hated drugs and the grief they brought. Richard liked a drink but nothing more. He hated drugs to the extent that he would disown his own children if they touched so much as a joint.

A mistake had been made, but it would be sorted soon. Richard had to focus on that thought. He didn't know what else he could do.

The night Ken won the lottery, Richard had been down at the Foundry getting drunk with his mates. As the call came through from Julie telling him to go to his dad's house, Richard was being pulled off a lad who he thought was being too rowdy.

The landlord had brought a karaoke machine in for the night, and Richard was belting out his own rendition of 'Crocodile Rock' by Elton John. A lad at the bar, the worse for wear after an evening celebrating his twenty-first birthday, started heckling him. Richard paused from his singing. 'I'll not be a minute,' he said into the microphone before handing it to the person standing closest to him.

Richard marched over to the heckler and picked him up by the scruff of his neck. Then he dragged him over to the nearest wall and pushed his head into a picture frame.

Within seconds Richard's back was covered in various pairs of hands trying to pull him off the birthday boy. As he felt his shirt rip along its back seam, Richard heard his name being called out from the bar.

'Chalky – phone,' the barman shouted over. The hands immediately released him.

'I'll have you after,' Richard snarled at the lad, now lying in a crumpled heap on the floor.

He spoke to Julie, who told him to go to Ken's. Richard grabbed his jacket, left the pub and ran the mile or so to his parents' home.

Ken was sat in his armchair when Richard walked into the house. Julie hadn't been able to tell him why his dad needed to see him so urgently. She had guessed he would have had plenty to drink by then and would probably have announced the win to the entire pub. As it was he simply returned to the bar later that night and announced it anyway.

'What's the crack then, Dad?' He was relieved to see him looking fit and well.

Ken waved his ticket at him. 'We've won the lottery,' he said, grinning at his son.

'Right, give it here then. Let's check your ticket.' Richard knew better than to get excited. His dad had thought he had got five numbers two weeks earlier before he realised he had checked off an old ticket.

He looked at the date first – it was for that week's draw. Then he called up the numbers on Teletext and checked them off himself. The numbers matched.

'Yeah, you're right. We have won,' he said, handing the ticket back to Ken. 'So what's happenin' then?'

Ken explained that he hadn't been able to get the

win confirmed yet, but they looked in line to pick up more than six million pounds. If that were true then the three sons would be getting a million pounds each.

'Hey! Nice one, Dad! Right – well, I'm not going to Spain then. Not with a million quid to celebrate. I'll soon sort it.'

Richard's wagon was already loaded up for a trip to Barcelona. He began ringing round other drivers he knew to take it for him. There was no way he would be working again for a while. He couldn't get a driver despite offering to let one of them keep the fifteen-thousand-pound wagon on his return. His problem was finally solved when the company Richard was driving for sent another driver up the following morning.

That night Richard started celebrating. During the months that followed it developed into a way of life as he stopped working and began to enjoy living the high life. To him the money was not something that should be invested for the future, tied up in stocks and shares. It was there to be spent and enjoyed for as long as it lasted. If, after a couple of years, he ended up broke, he didn't care. He just wanted some fun.

In time Richard would look back and reflect that, for him, a much smaller sum of money would have been better. Had he been given, say, a hundred thousand pounds – enough to pay off his mortgage, buy a car and go on holiday – he might never have ended up in a police cell in the first place.

Instead, with a million pounds in the bank, he quit work and spent his days drinking in bars with the new set of friends his money had bought. It was those friends and his new lifestyle that would eventually land him in court on trial for a million-pound drug-smuggling operation.

The cell door swung open and Richard jumped to his feet. He looked for his watch on his wrist before he remembered it had been taken off him by the custody sergeant. The lights had been switched on an hour earlier. That had felt like another affront to his dignity – not being able to choose whether he wanted his light on or off. The officer had his breakfast on a tray.

'Well, you can take that shit back with you. I'm not hungry.'

'Please yourself – but you'll get nothing else.' The police officer turned to leave.

'When am I getting out of here? Is my brief around?'

'Nothing to do with me, mate.' The door slammed shut again.

Richard revelled in playing the millionaire playboy and slipped into his new place in society quite comfortably. From day one he had seen three options open to him – he could follow David and use his million to step up the business ladder; he could stay at home and mind the kids, like Stephen; or he could take an extended holiday and see how long it would take him to spend the lot. He chose the third.

It was a break Richard felt he deserved. He was thirty-one years old and had spent the last fifteen years of his life working killer hours on the wagons. The money was a gift to be enjoyed. His brothers appeared to be spellbound by it – agonising over how it should be invested and fretting over the performance of their shares. Surely the whole point of money won without effort was to use it to live out your dreams and fantasies. It smacked of meanness to do anything less. If they ended up destitute within five years, well – so what? His father had invested the rest of his money wisely and made it clear there would be another million each for them to collect when he died. While he was alive he would hardly see his son and family on the streets. Whatever happened, Richard knew he could return to work when the cash ran out – but he had no intention of doing so before that happened.

Julie proved to be a loyal ally in his plans to spend, spend, spend. They had been together for eight years and had two children: Charlotte, whose fourth birthday two days after the win was all but forgotten in the excitement, and Ben, a twenty-four-month-old baby at the time.

Richard had seen his dad spend most of his married life kowtowing to his mother, something he had made clear to Julie, his girlfriend of eight years, that he could never subscribe to in his own relationships. He had watched Ken clean and cook for the family while Sheila languished in her bed through periods of deep depression. He, like his father, viewed depression as weakness – something that she could have conquered had she really wanted to. By taking over the household chores Richard thought Ken had made it easier for his mother to slip deeper into it. As a result he had vowed never to even pick up a duster, and Julie accepted that. His role within the family unit was clear – when they needed money he would work for it. When they had it to spare he would enjoy himself. As long as they had cash in the bank she had no problem with that.

Cash, he discovered quickly, was something you didn't need when you came into the kind of money they had. Within days of paying in his million-pound cheque a steady stream of credit-card agreements had landed on the doormat. He hadn't even had to fill in any forms – the banks had done that for him, with a cross marking where he should sign. He had always dealt in hard cash before the win; now he just had to hand over a piece of plastic and sign his name to buy anything he or Julie wanted. There was no need to even look at price tags. They could afford anything – reason wasn't part of the equation.

Holidays were no longer a treat but a way of killing time, with or without his family. He took Julie and the children abroad a dozen times during the next two years as well as taking frequent trips away with his mates.

Gifts for friends included fifteen-thousand-pound four-wheel-drive vehicles and Cartier watches. If Julie admired a ten-thousand-pound diamond ring in a jewellery shop window he would tell her she could have it as long as there was enough credit left on whichever card he pulled first from his wallet. He felt no shame or embarrassment if his card was rejected – it was simply a twist on the game he had created to make spending money even more fun.

Richard looked at the tray of food lying untouched on the cell floor. He hauled himself over to it, his back aching after an uncomfortable night on a hard bench. The coffee in its plastic cup was lukewarm. He forced himself to drink it.

It seemed like an age since his arrest, yet less than a day had passed. Richard and Julie had just arrived home from a family holiday in Jamaica when the police raided his house. Richard had gone to the nearest pub to meet some friends for a drink. Early in the evening he had noticed a police van pull up in the pub car-park. He had looked out of the window as two officers climbed out of the back of it. They had looked straight at him, then one of them began to talk into his police radio. Richard thought no more of it.

He had arranged for a taxi to pick him up and take him home for a quarter to midnight. As he pulled up outside his house he saw two men looking through the boot of Julie's Mercedes.

'What the fuck are you playing at?' he had yelled at them as he got out of the car.

Three more men came out of his house and began to walk towards him. One of the men looked up from the car boot. 'Are you Richard White?' he asked.

'Yeah – what the fuck is going on?'

'We're police officers,' he said, flashing his identity card. 'You'd better come inside.'

Richard's head was spinning. They seemed so aggressive that he knew immediately they weren't here to gently break news of some tragedy in the family. He was in some kind of trouble, but he had no idea what.

As he entered the house he could hear Julie talking to someone in the sitting room. She was telling him that they had two safes under the kitchen sink that they hadn't had chance to fit yet. She sounded exasperated. He began to walk into the room to join her but was guided into the kitchen.

'Richard White, I am arresting you on suspicion of conspiring to import illegal substances. Anything you have to say –'

Richard leant against the breakfast bar as he took in what the policeman was saying. It didn't make sense. He had no idea what he was talking about.

Once he had been cautioned, Richard asked what they were looking for as they searched the house. His children were asleep upstairs and thankfully hadn't woken. No one had gone into their bedrooms.

They were looking for drugs and large sums of money. Richard began to relax – they would find nothing like that in his house. He rarely used cash because it was easier to spend on his credit cards. And there were certainly no drugs on the premises.

'Can I talk to my wife?'

The policeman laughed. 'No, you can't. But you do need to talk to your solicitor. Now get your coat and we'll get down to the station so you can be interviewed.'

Richard did as they said. 'You'll at least let me say goodbye to her.'

Julie was sitting on the sofa. She looked up at him. 'Are you all right, love?' she asked.

He smiled back at her, desperate to reassure her despite being as confused himself. 'I've got to go down to the station and sort this mess out. I'll see you in the morning, love.'

She began to cry. 'Come on, Julie. It's all right. I'll answer their questions and I'll come home. Just don't let the kids pick up on any of this. They'll never need to know. Ring my dad and tell him what's going on. He'll be able to help.'

* * *

Richard's lifestyle had changed beyond recognition after he got his million off his father. Despite having a business to run, he spent most of his time drinking in bars and clubs. He put one of his closest friends in charge of his haulage business, JR Plant Services, to free him to do just that. The business had already been going for four years prior to the win but had been struggling to keep financially viable. Richard had propped it up with some of the lottery money, expecting it to give him a return when the rest of the cash ran out. While he had made a conscious decision to spend his money on enjoying himself he hadn't expected to spend as much time away from work as he eventually did. But he quickly discovered a way of life he never before even knew existed, and being part of it became almost an addiction.

At first he simply went drinking in the Foundry through the week, whereas before his long hours on the road meant he could indulge in that pleasure only at the weekends. He started making his way down there at lunchtime and would remain until closing time.

The month after the win he and his family had moved into a hundred-and-fifty-thousand-pound house in Glazebury. Richard then discovered new pubs to drink in – and new drinking partners.

Richard found he had stepped up a league. Instead of passing time with people who were in the pubs in Leigh because they were out of work, he was now drinking with people who simply didn't need to work. Either they had their own legitimate businesses and, like Richard, employed other people to run them or, as the rest of his family kept telling him, they were criminals. Either way Richard didn't care.

They were good company and he wasn't about to start grilling them about how they came by their money.

Richard's life – social and domestic – had revolved around Leigh ever since they moved there. He had travelled most of Europe on his wagon, but that was work – he was usually too exhausted on long-haul trips to take in much of the country he was in.

His new friends introduced him to Manchester and ways of passing time that only the wealthy could afford. He felt at ease with these people. For the first time since the win Richard found he was just one of a group who could afford to spend their afternoons drinking champagne and watching the world go by. Instead of feeling obliged to foot the bill for the people whose company he was enjoying, he found himself under no pressure to get his credit card out. His new companions were even faster off the mark than he was to order a couple of bottles of champagne.

Julie was incredibly tolerant of Richard's behaviour, which she viewed as simply a short-term period he had to go through as he got used to the new direction their lives were taking. She, too, enjoyed spending the money and, while she would have liked to join him as he wined and dined day after day, she had to stay at home and look after their children. But Richard quickly began to lose control and, just weeks into this new lifestyle, he pushed the boundaries and Julie's patience too far.

One afternoon, as he was on his way to meet his friends in Manchester, his mobile phone rang. It was Julie. She sounded upset and wanted him to return home immediately. She refused to tell him what the problem was, but he knew by her tone that it was serious. He drove straight home.

As he walked into the house Julie was sitting at the kitchen table, a pile of bank and credit-card statements in front of her. She looked up at him, her face stained with mascara from where she had been crying. She wasn't crying now, though. She looked furious.

'What the fuck is this, Richard? What the hell have you been doing?' She waved one of the sheets of paper at him.

'What are you talking about? Christ – what is this?' He had no idea what she could be so upset about. He began to take off his jacket.

'Don't bother taking your coat off, Richard. You're not stopping.'

'You what? What's going on?'

Julie began to cry. She passed a credit-card statement to him, pointing out a line that showed he had paid for a room at the Ramada Hotel in Manchester a month earlier. Richard felt a wave of nausea pass over him as he realised what she had discovered.

He had been certain that Julie would never find out what he had done that night, when a day of drinking had spilt on into the night and he had ended up in a hotel room with a woman he had never met before and would doubtless never see again.

He had had lunch at the Istanbul that day and had then gone on to the Fantasy Bar, a lap-dancing joint in the town centre, with the regular crowd. The champagne had been flowing, and they had gone from there to a nearby club to spend the evening. As usual, their table was like a magnet to single women in the club. There was always a steady stream of bottles of bubbly being brought over to them, and they were hardly discreet as they opened them. Normally Richard would simply chat with these girls, never going beyond harmless flirting.

But for some reason – and Richard still couldn't fathom why – this night he took it further. The woman hadn't been particularly attractive, but she was very forward. Even through the alcohol-induced blur she was clearly coming on to him.

There had been little conversation between them. He had made no pretence of enjoying her company, finding it far more amusing to pass sarcastic comments about people on the dance floor with his friends. But every time he turned around, there she was, smiling at him or laughing at one of his jokes.

'You told me you stayed at a mate's house that night,' Julie bellowed at him. 'You didn't – you went to a fucking hotel with some tart. Well? Didn't you? It's here in black and white.'

'Are you asking me or telling me, Julie?'

Julie began to laugh and cry at the same time. 'Stop the fucking games, Richard. Just tell me the truth.'

The truth was that at the end of the evening this woman – he thought her name was Linda or Tracy, but he couldn't be sure – had asked him if he wanted to book into a hotel for some fun. He'd barely thought about the consequences – he was drunk and still on a high from the win and the way his life had changed. He felt invincible, as if he could do what he liked when he liked without anyone being able to restrict him. Going off with this woman seemed to symbolise that.

He'd regretted it like hell the next morning, when he saw this stranger lying next to him in the hotel bedroom. He had been overwhelmed with guilt and surprised at just how little attraction he felt for her in the cold light of day, whereas the night before the very fact that she wasn't Julie made having sex with her an exciting thing to do. The irony was, now he'd done it, he wished to God it was Julie he had woken up with. The woman had rolled towards him, sensing he had woken up. He had jumped out of bed, pulled on his clothes and walked out of the door before she had even properly woken up. He had paid the bill with a credit card and left, telling Julie he had stayed at a friend's house.

Julie hadn't questioned him when he had arrived back home. He had gone missing several times in the weeks before, and she had given up worrying where he was. She trusted him and that had, in a way, made it easier to lie. He thought he had got away with it.

'All right, I'll tell you the truth. If that's what you want?' He was giving her a chance to drop the whole thing, but he knew she wouldn't take it.

'Just tell me, Richard.'

'All right. Yeah – I took some tart back to a hotel and I shagged her. Happy?' He put his jacket back on and walked out of the house.

He had driven into Manchester in a daze. Julie might have been tolerant of his behaviour so far, but he knew she would never stand for this. He had to face up to the distinct possibility that she would leave him – taking his children with her.

It took weeks of pleading for her to even consider staying with him. She had even spoken to someone at a Citizens Advice Bureau about how much of his money she would be entitled to if they did split up. As it turned out it would have been very little – but that wasn't an issue. His father had already assured her that she would get something off the family if she did leave him.

But Richard loved Julie, and he knew deep down that, despite what he had done, she loved him. He had to find a way of proving to her that he had made a mistake and that he was desperately sorry.

David had been in a similar situation when they first won the money. His wife had also wanted to separate. At the time he had pointed out to his brother that, with the kind of money they had come into, he could make a great life for himself as a single man. David had dismissed that suggestion and now he understood why. What was the point of living the high life with no one to share some normality with?

His final bid to get Julie back was by asking her to marry him. She had been shocked at first but eventually came round to the idea. He had always been so against them getting married, but now he couldn't think of anything he wanted more.

'I promise you, Julie, it was one stupid mistake. I'll never do it again.'

Julie amazed him by her response. 'I know it was,' she said calmly. 'I know you wouldn't be stupid enough to risk it again because you know that then it really would be over.'

'It was just a moment of madness. I can't even remember her name.'

Julie had explained that the only way she could accept what had happened was by telling herself over and over that at least he hadn't had an affair. Her other great love, apart from her family, had always been horses. She told him that she saw him as behaving like a horse that had been locked up for months in stables and then suddenly had been let out to run wild. It would kick and run and fall over a few times before finding its feet again. She understood that he needed some freedom to go out and be a bit crazy for a while. She felt he was entitled to that. But what she did resent was the way he went about it – he had lied to her and betrayed her and she could tolerate that only once.

The wedding had been a sumptuous affair, his dad in his element making sure everything was perfect for them. For a while Richard did curb his behaviour, but he soon slipped back into his old ways, frittering his time and money away in trendy bars in Manchester. But he stayed away from other women. There was a marriage at stake now, and Julie would never trust him again if he let her down. If he wanted to carry on living like a playboy and getting away with it, he had to acknowledge the boundaries and stick with them. He could only rely on Julie's trust to a point.

The trips abroad with his friends continued, so that Richard was away more than he was at home. He knew Julie could cope with that – after all, she had put up with him driving long distances all the time they had been together. They also went on holidays together, and she had unlimited access to their bank accounts. Neither of them kept a close watch on how much money was left. Their home and cars were paid for, and his dad was looking after the children's school fees. Richard's philosophy was that as long as they had a roof over their heads that was paid for, it wouldn't really matter when the money ran out.

So for the time being Richard rarely went into the office, confident that the people he employed would keep the business running smoothly. They would be able to contact him on his mobile with any problems. At least that was what he had thought. Now, as he sat in the police cell waiting for something to happen, he wondered for the first time if that had been wise. The detectives seemed to think that his business was involved with the crimes they were accusing him of – they had taken all papers connected with JR Plant Services from the house. But he was so far removed from the business these days that he had no idea how it was operating, and if anything underhand had been going on he wouldn't have a clue. He just hoped that the police and Customs & Excise men would be able to see that for themselves.

Chapter Six

RICHARD LOOKED TOWARDS THE CELL DOOR – he could hear voices outside it. One belonged to the duty officer who had brought him his breakfast; he recognised the other as his solicitor, Aiden Carr.

Richard felt a moment of relief when he realised Aiden had arrived. Things would start moving now. Aiden had already got him out of one sticky mess earlier in the year when he had been set to lose his driving licence. Richard knew he could trust him to get him out of the mess he was in now.

Aiden briefed Richard on what was happening. He explained that he was one of thirteen people who had been arrested. He mentioned some names of the others being questioned at different police stations across the city. Richard recognised a couple of them through business dealings in the past. One stood out as being part of the crowd he went drinking with in Manchester; the rest were strangers.

'They've picked up a vehicle with one and a half million quid's worth of cannabis in it at a farm,' Aiden explained. Richard recognised the registration – it was one of his, which, as far as he knew, was out on hire. 'They reckon you're involved.'

'I don't know a fucking thing about it. What do we do now?'

'You go in and answer their questions. We'll take it from there.'

Aiden couldn't sit in on the interview because he was needed across town. There was a knock on the cell door and one of Aiden's colleagues, Adrian Lovatt, walked in. 'Adrian'll take over from here,' said Aiden. 'You'll be all right with him.'

Richard walked into the interview room, his heart pounding with anticipation. He was certain that once he had answered their questions he would be allowed home. A table was pushed up against the side wall with a tape deck plugged into one of two sockets. There was a window on the far wall, but it was too small and high up to light the room. Someone pressed a switch on the wall behind him and harsh fluorescent light flickered into action.

Adrian and his assistant, Julia Millington, sat on one side of the table; Detective Constable John McEwan, from the Regional Crime Squad, and Nicholas Shaw, from Customs & Excise's National Investigation Service, introduced themselves and sat on the other. DC McEwan switched on the tape recorder and explained that an interview was taking place, which might later be used in any court case that could follow. The three other people introduced themselves for the benefit of the tape, and Richard was asked to state his name and date of birth.

At first they just wanted details about who he was and the names of his wife and children. When it came to giving his address, the police officer asked him where he had lived before moving to Glazebury.

'Okey-dokey,' he said, after Richard had told him. 'Without sounding condescending, there's a marked difference between the two houses.'

Richard nodded and explained about the lottery win. He was certain they already knew all about it, but Aiden's advice had stuck. He had to answer every question honestly and without fuss. Then he would be able to go home.

Richard began to relax as questions were fired at him. They wanted to know about his business and how it was run. It seemed clear to him that he had very little involvement in the day-to-day running of it.

He was shown documents detailing van and lorry hire arrangements made through his business. It gradually became clear that one of his wagons that had been out on hire had been used to smuggle cannabis into the country.

A false bulkhead had been fitted inside it to create a secret compartment. Inside that had been placed three hundred and three one-kilogramme blocks of cannabis resin which were brought into the country from Spain.

Richard continued to explain that he knew very little about how his business was being run, holding his hands up to the kind of lifestyle he had been leading. He told them repeatedly that he had left other people in charge at JR Plant Services while he enjoyed a break from work. They seemed to reject this from the word go, insisting that he had used his lottery money to fund the entire operation.

Richard returned to his cell exhausted. He had been on autopilot for the last few hours, answering questions as they were fired at him. He hadn't had chance to worry about the answers he was giving – he had been too busy concentrating on what was being said. He faced another sleepless night without any contact with his family. Somehow he would have to get through it.

The next morning Richard was driven to Manchester magistrates' court, where the police and Customs people would ask to hold him for questioning for another twenty-four hours. He was handcuffed to a guard throughout the journey and inside the courtroom. He felt grubby – he still hadn't been able to shower and was wearing the same clothes he was arrested in.

The hearing lasted only a few minutes, and they were soon back at the police station, where the questions continued.

By the end of the day Richard had been asked 1,605 questions. He answered every one of them.

As the tape was switched off he realised his interrogation had come to an end. They were letting him go.

He began to sigh with relief, but the feeling was short-lived.

'Richard White, I am now charging you with . . .'

At that point Richard's mind shut down with exhaustion and confusion. It wasn't over – it was just beginning.

Richard walked back into the interview room where he felt he had lived for the last two days. Julie and Ken were sitting where the two officers had been before them. They were both staring at the ground in silence.

'I'll be just outside,' the guard told Richard, leaving the door wide open.

Their heads shot up and Julie burst into tears. She jumped to her feet and threw herself into his arms.

As he felt the warmth of her body against him he began to weep. 'I'm so sorry,' he sobbed. 'I don't know what's happening – I just don't know what's going on here.'

His dad put his arm around Richard's shoulders and patted him firmly. Richard looked at his father – he looked old and grey for the first time in his life.

'Are you involved, son?' Ken asked gently.

Richard shook his head. 'No, Dad, I promise you. This has got nothing to do with me.'

Ken nodded back at him. 'Then we'll stand by you. Whatever it takes – we'll get you out of here.' The three of them cried together. No one could think of anything else to say or do.

They left after an hour. Julie had brought some clean clothes for him, and he was finally allowed to shower. Despite the fact that he had actually been charged, Richard felt a little better. The guards seemed to treat him with more respect now that the interviewing had finished.

'You're up to your eyes in this, aren't you, son?' said one of the guards as he took Richard's fingerprints.

Richard looked him in the eye. 'Nothing I need to worry about, mate,' he replied. 'It'll all come out in the wash.'

'We'll see,' he said back. 'You're off to the magistrates next – you're up there first thing in the morning.'

Richard felt relieved. He could say goodbye to the miserable cell, where he had spent the last two nights. Then, tomorrow, he would get bail and finally go home.

* * *

Richard put his hand across his mouth and nose as the door of his new cell slammed shut behind him. It was partly to keep the smell out of his nostrils and partly to keep the bile that had risen into his mouth from coming out.

His previous cell was like a hotel bedroom compared with this place. It stank – there was no lavatory, but its previous occupants had obviously just used the floor. The walls were covered in graffiti. It took all his powers of self-control to stop himself from vomiting on the spot as he took a closer look. It was daubed on with human excrement.

Richard sat on the bench that was supposed to be his bed and drew his knees up into his chest. He had to get through this – he had no choice. Tomorrow he would be going home.

Chapter Seven

RICHARD STOOD ON THE LANDING outside the courtroom where the magistrates inside had just refused him bail. He was surrounded by his co-accused, yet he didn't recognise any of them.

Richard didn't speak to anyone – he was too bewildered to even think about striking up a conversation.

The magistrates had refused him bail on two grounds, the first that he could interfere with witnesses and the second that he was wealthy enough to abscond. He could see their point on the second reason, but who the hell was he likely to interfere with? He didn't know the first thing about this huge crime he was supposed to have helped mastermind, never mind who the witnesses to it were.

Richard had been certain that he would get bail and be on his way home by now. He had been stunned when he realised that wouldn't be happening. Instead, he was waiting for a van to collect him and take him to Strangeways, the prison that had become a battleground between prisoners and warders eight years earlier. The place might have been rebuilt since then, but its name remained synonymous with misery. However bad last night had been, he was certain that what lay ahead of him would be much worse.

The bus arrived and they were ushered towards the lift to take them down. A tall dark-haired man slipped one end of a pair of handcuffs on to one of his wrists and clicked it shut. The other was already around Richard's.

In court he had been introduced as Martin Lennon from Customs & Excise – he was in charge of the whole investigation. He hadn't taken his eyes off Richard throughout the short hearing.

'I believe you've come into some money, Mr White,' said Lennon sarcastically as they got into the lift.

'Oh, aye,' said Richard. 'Plenty enough to sue you lot.'

Lennon laughed. 'We'll see.'

'Yeah, we will.'

Lennon led him towards the van. 'Enjoy your stay, mate!'

Richard forced himself to grin back at him. He made a mental note of his name. If that guy had got some kind of personal problem with him he would pay for it after the trial. However bad it got from now, Richard knew one thing – he would have his day in court. Then, when he was acquitted, the writs would fly.

The prison van pulled off the main Bury New Road leading out of Manchester. The windows were darkened so that no one could see in but the prisoners could still see out. The heavy iron door leading into Strangeways rolled aside to let them in. Richard felt his entire body sink into the seat, the

direness of his situation hitting home as the door
clanked shut behind them. Another door rolled open,
and the bus drove through it before stopping to let
them out.

Richard had driven past this place so many times
without even thinking of what it might be like inside.
Now he was here as an inmate.

The prisoners were led off the van one at a time,
handcuffed to a guard until they reached the
booking-in desk. There the cuffs were removed while
the guard returned to the van for the next prisoner.
Richard gave brief details of his address and date of
birth.

In return Richard was given a prisoner number and
told he should make a phone call home so that he
could give it to Julie. Anyone wanting to contact him
while he was inside would have to give that number.

Richard jumped at the chance to speak to his wife.
He had thought about her so many times since their
brief visit the day before. He felt utterly alone,
unable to speak to his own wife without seeking
permission first.

She wasn't there, but Richard left a message for
her with his brother-in-law Robert. He came away
from the telephone feeling even more dejected,
wondering when they would next speak.

At another desk Richard's fingerprints were taken,
along with a set of photographs. He had to stifle a
laugh as he held up a card with his identity number
across it. The whole thing felt surreal. He
half-expected someone to jump out from behind a
door and announce that the whole thing had just
been an elaborate hoax to make him look foolish.

The whole process was taking hours, but Richard

was in no hurry. The longer it took before he was shown to his cell the better. He didn't know what to expect, but from previous experience he knew he should prepare himself for the worst.

He was put in a holding cell as he waited for the next stage. Around a dozen men were in there, mostly leaning against the walls smoking, or catching up with previous acquaintances. The only entertainment was a Turkish guy in the corner who was throwing up on his own feet. He was shaking, and his face was grey. Richard guessed he was suffering withdrawal symptoms from whatever drugs he was on.

'White – you're next.' The greatest affront to his dignity was still to take place. He had to be strip-searched before he could be taken into the cell-block where he had been assigned.

He walked into yet another small room, his eyes instantly drawn to the curtain in one corner.

'Get behind there and take your clothes off,' the guard said. Richard was amazed by how matter-of-fact he sounded.

Richard went behind the curtain and started to untie his shoelaces. He had always had at the back of his mind an idea that something like this would happen. He had forced himself not to dwell on it. But now it was actually about to happen and there was absolutely nothing he could do to stop it.

He looked up. The guard was also behind the curtain looking straight at him, his arms folded in front of him.

'OK – pass me your shoes.'

Richard did as he was asked. The guard made no comments other than to tell him which piece of clothing to take off next. He seemed like a decent enough guy, and Richard could tell he took no pleasure from this part of his job. He made an incredibly unnatural situation as comfortable as it ever could be.

The guard examined every piece of his clothing, patting it down on the table next to them to check that nothing was hidden inside.

Then came the moment he hadn't even dared to imagine. The guard pulled two plastic gloves from a packet on the table and began to put them on his hands.

Richard stood wearing just his T-shirt.

'OK – turn round and squat down.'

'You what?' Richard laughed nervously. 'You're joking, aren't you?'

'Just get on with it, lad.'

Richard did as he said. The only way he could handle what was being done to him now was by making out it was no big deal. If he reacted any differently then he might as well give up the fight now. His day would come – he had to keep telling himself that.

He tried to remove himself from what was happening. He emptied his mind until it was over. For the first time in his life he understood what women meant when they said they felt as though someone had treated them like a piece of meat.

Richard's cell was in K-wing. Prisoners here were locked up for twenty-three hours a day. Before he was shown inside, Richard was introduced to the guard who patrolled his landing.

'Right, sonny. House rules,' said the guard; 'you call officers, male or female, gov or boss. You don't give any lip. You treat us with respect and you'll be all right. Give us any trouble and you'll get some back. Understood?'

Richard nodded in reply. He had no intention of giving anyone any trouble.

Richard held his breath as the door opened. By the standards of the last few days he was pleasantly surprised by what greeted him.

The cell was clean, for a start. There was a bunk-bed pushed up against a wall, and sprawled out on the bottom bed was his roommate.

'You're sharing with Peters here,' said the warder. 'He'll show you the ropes.'

Peters, a black man with long dreadlocks, raised his right hand in greeting. His smile was warm – Richard instantly felt relieved. The way his luck had been going recently he had been convinced his cellmate would turn out to be some hard-case pervert who would make his life hell.

The cell was a marked improvement on any of the others he had been in since Wednesday night. There was a proper lavatory, although still no privacy. 'Just let us know when you need a shit and I'll look away,' Peters explained.

Richard was to have the top bunk. It had clean sheets and blankets in a pile ready for him to make up his bed. He was used to living in luxury with a cleaner to change the sheets at home. Yet right now just the sight of a clean sheet made him feel like his luck was turning.

He had his own shelf above the desk, and there were two chairs where he and Peters would spend much of the days that followed. At the moment all he had to put on the shelf were the comb, toothbrush, toothpaste and sachet of shampoo that came in the prison starter pack he was handed on his way in.

He would have to get Julie to pay some money into his prison account so that he would have some money to spend in the tuck shop. There he would be able to buy toiletries and something to read to pass the time.

Richard lay down on his bunk, and his spirits soared as he noticed he had his own spotlight with a switch he could control himself. He could never have imagined, before all this, how important a detail like that could be to him. But it was one piece of control in a world that had gone completely mad around him. It made him feel a little bit better – something he was desperate to build on.

In the days that followed, Richard filled the great stretches of time in the cell talking to Peters and, for the first time since school, reading. He had never had time to pick up a book with the hours he spent out on the road. Since the win he'd been too busy spending his money to sit in a chair reading.

He thought of his mother – for her, reading had become an obsession. Peters had lent Richard a book about Fred and Rose West written by her daughter. It was nothing like the kind of book Sheila would have chosen – she preferred trashy romances. He smiled to himself as he considered the kind of reaction he would get in Strangeways if he had a Mills & Boon paperback under his pillow.

He wondered how Sheila had taken the news. He knew he was in for a roasting when he saw her. He didn't care about that, though – he just wanted her to know that he was sorry for any grief he had brought on the family but that it wasn't his fault.

Peters was good to Richard, who was grateful to him for that.

Richard was amazed by how much Peters knew about him and the people he was charged with. But information, like cigarettes, was a form of currency inside, where anonymity didn't exist.

The prisoners in K-wing were, apart from their three visits a week, totally cut off from the outside world. They left their cells for an hour each day in two separate shifts. They didn't get to watch the news – the highlight of the day, Richard discovered, was if you got your hour out in the evening. That way you could watch *Coronation Street* or catch one half of a football match if there was one on.

The rest of the day was spent filling time – looking for anything to break up the day. A trip to court, despite the indignities it involved with further strip-searches on the way in and out, provided a change in routine and something to look forward to. Even though he was refused bail at two further hearings, they were at least a break from prison life.

Every morning, when he awoke from a night peppered with bad dreams and thoughts of his family, he told himself he would be going home that day. He focused on the fact that a mistake had been made and that Julie and his dad would be working flat out to get him released.

Richard had little contact with the other prisoners. He knew he had landed on his feet getting put in a cell with Peters, but he didn't want to risk crossing anyone else in the block. He was a social novice in this place and didn't know the rules well enough to play the game. He knew that his safest option was to keep his head down and attract as little attention to himself as possible.

One evening, as he queued for the telephone so he could call Julie, one of the other prisoners began to stare at him. Richard had just collected some bits from the tuck shop and had them in his hands. He had seen this big bruiser of a man bully some of the other prisoners into giving him what few belongings they had. Now he had his eye on Richard's phone card.

He began to move towards Richard, who braced himself for a confrontation. He was just weighing up his options when Peters appeared from nowhere and took the other guy to one side. Peters spoke quietly into his ear, and his would-be tormentor immediately stepped back away from them.

'Listen – sorry, mate. No harm done,' he said to Richard, holding up his hands.

Later, in their cell, Richard asked Peters what he had said to him.

'I just let him know who your co-accused are. You'll get no trouble in here from now on.'

After two weeks inside, Richard's request for bail was taken to a judge in chambers. He wasn't allowed out for this hearing and would have to wait for news from his warders. The prosecution told the bail hearing that Richard was the paymaster and had used his lottery money to fund the whole thing. They argued that he should not be released because the levels of cash available to him made it highly likely that he would abscond. Bail was finally set at 1.15 million pounds.

* * *

'OK, lads. If you two come up with two hundred and fifty thousand each, I'll put the rest up,' Ken said to Stephen and David after the hearing.

'You must be fucking joking,' sneered Stephen. 'I'm not paying anything to get him out.'

'Hang on a minute,' said Ken, who had presumed the three of them would be pulling together to get Richard out. 'He's your brother – you have to help get him out.'

'Look, Dad – how many times was he warned that he was hanging around with the wrong kinds of people? How many times did we tell him to get his act together before he ended up in trouble? He told us all to keep our noses out. Well, if the stupid little bastard wants to hang out with criminals, then Strangeways is the best bloody place for him.'

Stephen left. Ken spoke to David: 'What about you, then?' He and Richard's solicitor looked at him intently.

'Yeah – I'll stump up the money. But only because blood's thicker than water. Stephen's right – we did tell him, and he took no notice. He didn't give a shit.'

Then David turned to the solicitor. 'What happens to me money if Richard runs off?'

'You what?' yelled Ken, barely able to contain his fury. 'How can you say he'd run off?'

'Well, why not, Dad? He's always run away from his problems. What happens if he runs away from this one? I want to know how to protect my money if I find out he's planning to jump on a plane out of the country.'

'If you knew he was going to abscond then, as long as you informed the police immediately, your money would be safe,' the solicitor explained.

'He's not going to run off anywhere,' said Ken angrily. 'He's done nothing wrong, so why should he go anywhere?'

He turned to David. 'I'm disgusted with you and your brother. You don't talk about family like that. You stick together in a crisis – I thought you both knew that.'

'Oh, get away, Dad. You just can't see it, can you? Our Richard is dragging us all through the mud. Yeah, I'll stand by him because he's my brother, but it doesn't mean I have to pretend I'm not fucking furious with him for the way he's behaved. He doesn't give a shit about anyone but himself in all of this, and you just can't see it.'

Early in the afternoon Richard was told to get his things together. He was being moved to C-wing, a lower-security section of the prison.

'This is it, mate,' he told Peters, sweeping his collection of belongings off his shelf. There were a couple of potnoodles and a new bottle of shampoo among some other toiletries. He gave everything to Peters.

In C-wing he wasn't put into a cell but allowed to hang around in the large common room. He paced up and down as he waited for news from the court.

''Scuse me, gov,' he called over as one of the warders passed him. 'Any news for me?'

'If you've heard nothing by three o'clock you know you're stopping,' he replied. It was half-past two.

Richard went over to the payphone. He had enough credit on his card to splash out on a call to Julie's mobile. She answered after a couple of rings.

'Be quick, Julie,' he said. 'Is there any news?'

'You're coming out,' she said, sounding startled by his voice. 'We've been waiting outside for you since eleven o'clock this morning.'

At that moment he heard his prison number being called out.

'You're off home,' the warder mouthed at him as he looked over.

Richard whooped down the phone. 'I'm coming out, Julie! He's just told me, I'm coming out!'

He heard Julie begin to cry into her mobile. 'Stop crying, Julie. There's no need for any more of that. The tide's turned, love. Now it's my turn to make these tossers look stupid.'

Outside the prison Julie flung herself into his arms. His dad looked weary but elated to have his youngest son out of prison. It had cost Ken more than a million pounds of surety to get Richard out, and he assured him immediately that he had got him the best defence team that money could buy.

'We'll have our day, lad – we'll have it in court,' he said confidently. 'Somehow they're going to have to make this up to you, and I'm going to make damned sure they do.'

As they walked away Richard turned back for another look at the prison. His taste of life inside had been better than he'd expected in some ways, but in others it had been worse than anything he could ever have imagined. But he had got through it. He just prayed he would never have to return.

Chapter Eight

ON THE DAY OF RICHARD'S RELEASE, Stephen White walked into the hallway as his wife Susan was coming down the stairs. She paused halfway down and waited for him to speak.

He looked at her and shook his head. He couldn't think what to say.

'Well,' she said finally, 'is he out, then?' She continued her descent, following Stephen into the lounge, where he threw himself on one of the sofas.

'Oh, yeah, he's out, all right. Me dad made sure of that.'

'What do you mean?'

'Oh, he's only put up more than a million quid bail to get him out. Can you believe it? A million pounds.' Stephen leant forward and buried his head in his hands.

'Stephen, it must be bad if they set bail so high. I thought it was all supposed to be some kind of mix-up. What the hell has he got involved with?'

Stephen leant back into the cushions and sighed, wearily shaking his head. 'They think he's some Mr Big who's been running the whole thing. They're saying he's used the lottery money to fund it. It's a nightmare.'

'So what happens now?'

Stephen laughed. 'Oh, now my dad's throwing as much money as he can get his hands on to get him the best legal team money can buy. I tell you, Susan, if Richard goes down, this could take everything Dad's got.'

Susan moved over to the sofa and sat down next to him. 'It'll be all right, Stephen. Your brother gets himself out of every mess he finds himself in.'

'Oh, Susan, it's not just Richard and the money that's the issue here. My dad looks ill with the worry it all. There's Mum to think about as well. They must be going through hell. I don't know if even Richard will get himself out of trouble this time. There's going to be a trial now. We'll be plastered all over the papers again. What's that going to do to us – to the kids?'

Susan took his hands in hers and pressed them together. 'Whatever happens, we'll be all right,' she told him. 'Let your dad do whatever he feels he has to for Richard. We've got our own children to think about, and we'll do whatever we think is best for them. We'll make sure that this doesn't affect them.'

But Stephen knew that his brother's arrest had already affected their four daughters. The story had been on the front page of the *Sun* and as a result the girls had been teased about it at school.

Locally, news of Richard's arrest was providing great gossip for everyone who knew of them. They had moved to Culcheth expecting some privacy, hoping that the local community would accept them without needing to know anything about their lottery background. He and Susan had shied away from publicity from the word go. Now, with the photographs from when they first won the lottery all over the newspapers again, they were back in the news.

Their reasons for not wanting any more attention drawn to them had been simple. They were private people and, once the initial interest in the White family had died down, they felt they were entitled to some privacy. His mother had felt the same. Now, with this latest episode in their lives up for public consumption in the papers and the trial that would follow, that was impossible.

Stephen and Susan saw that people had an odd perception of lottery winners. The majority played the game each week and lost, and there seemed to be a general swing of mood against those who won. It was as though they thought that, because lottery winners had done nothing to earn their money, they weren't entitled to the same level of respect as other wealthy people. If you won the lottery then the nation seemed to feel you had taken their money. People felt entitled to pass comment when things went wrong, as though it was tough justice for the good fortune that came before. They also seemed to look on lottery money as free money, and because of that those who got it would always spend it recklessly. That wasn't Stephen's style.

Stephen knew exactly what Susan had meant when she talked about doing what was best for the children. Long before they won the lottery money they had dreamt of emigrating to Australia. They knew as soon as his father gave them the million pounds that they would go. Stephen had taken his family there soon after the win on an extended holiday to look into various business options. They had planned to return within the next twelve months.

In Australia no one would have to know anything about the life they would be leaving behind. Anyone who wanted to know the background to their wealth would be told it came from the haulage business they once owned. Chances were that nobody would even ask.

'We could always emigrate earlier,' he said, staring out of the window. He turned to look at his wife. 'What do you think, Susan? There's nothing to stop us getting away from here well before the trial even starts. That way we can start afresh and no one will need to know anything about what's happening here.'

'I think we should go for it,' she said. 'The last thing we need is to be dragged down by all this. I say we pack our bags and go.'

Stephen had first heard of his brother's arrest in a phone call from Susan. She had been staying with his parents in South Wales, at the house Ken had bought for Sheila's mother, when Ken had taken a call from Julie telling him what had happened. Susan rang Stephen to tell him that she would be returning early with his father who would be trying to get Richard out of prison.

He had been horrified by the news. He and David, along with his parents, had long been concerned about the lifestyle Richard had been enjoying ever since he received his share of the lottery payout. They had repeatedly told Richard that he was heading for disaster. However, none of them could have predicted that he would end up on trial for such a serious crime.

The family had long commented on the way Richard's loyalty to his friends verged on stupidity. They seemed to have a hold over him that no one, not even his wife Julie, could break. He had always been like that, from childhood through to adulthood. He would follow his friends into whatever kind of trouble they led him into and then live with the consequences.

Stephen also had to carry the burden of not being certain that his brother was innocent. Knowing the influence these new friends of his had on him, he couldn't credit his brother with having the sense not to get involved with whatever dodgy activities they were into. But drugs – that just didn't seem Richard's style.

He had confronted his brother with these doubts when he had been released on bail. Stephen had asked Richard to tell him if he was truly innocent. He told him he suspected he was pushing the 'guilt by association' line to get himself out of trouble. Richard had taken that as yet another opportunity to wind him up, telling Stephen he would have to wait for the trial to find out.

Stephen thought back over the fortnight his brother had spent in prison. He was certain Richard wouldn't have been so confident then. There had been many nights when Stephen had thought of him, bedding down in a prison cell, not knowing when he would see his children again. He had felt for him – worried about him, even. But during daylight he would remember the snide remarks Richard would make about his own life and that warmth and concern would vanish.

Any time Stephen had criticised him for the way he was living, Richard would taunt him over every aspect of his own life. He would tell him he was boring and downtrodden. But as far as Stephen was concerned he was living an honest, decent life that revolved around his wife and four daughters. He believed that Richard's scathing comments simply highlighted the lack of depth in his own relationships.

Stephen didn't know when or how his relationship with his younger brother had turned sour. As children they had been close, but once they hit adolescence they seemed to go off at completely different tangents.

David had remained close to both of them, always sidestepping trouble while still managing to get his point across. Stephen still couldn't work out quite how he managed to do that.

But the fact that they were brothers meant everything to David. He was as loyal to his family as Richard was to his mates. While Stephen applauded David for that, it was something he could not subscribe to.

Their parents had expected him and David to each put up some of the bail money. David had handed over a quarter of a million pounds, although with some reservations. Stephen had refused. He had not been prepared to pledge his family's future on backing a brother who had no respect for him or his values. He knew what the consequences would be when he said no – he'd had to deal with his father's anger at the time, and he expected that his refusal would mark the death knell for him and his brother. At that moment he didn't really care.

* * *

Now Richard was released on bail, Stephen and David arranged to meet up with him at Ken's house. Richard arrived first.

'Your mother's not happy, son.'

'I know, Dad. Listen – they've got me guilty by association. I'm not a drug dealer – I hate drugs, you know that. But I'm sorry for all this.'

'I know, lad, I know. But you have been bloody stupid. You've done the family name harm whether it was your fault or not. You know what people are like. If you throw enough shit at the wall it'll stick. It'll be hard for us to live this one down.'

Ken took him through to the living room, where Sheila was watching the television. She switched it off.

'What kind of shame have you brought on us now?' she asked.

'I'm sorry, Mum. I didn't mean any of this to happen.'

'Everyone knows. It's been all over the papers. How could you have been so stupid?'

'Look, Mum, I'm sorry. But you know I didn't do any of it. It's not my fault.'

'We told you to sort yourself out, but you ignored us. It doesn't matter that you didn't do it – you've still ruined our good name. You were too busy running around Manchester being some Champagne Charlie when you should have been at home with Julie and the kids.'

She turned to Ken. 'You said he'd be all right, that he'd calm down. Look how bloody wrong you were.' She stood up and walked to the door, catching sight of her other sons walking across the garden. 'Your brothers are here now. Let's see what you've got to say to them.'

* * *

Stephen glared at his younger brother. He clearly couldn't trust himself to speak first.

'Well, you're a fucking superstar you, aren't you?' said David as he sat down.

'What's that supposed to mean?' sneered Richard. 'Thanks a lot, brother.'

'You fucking idiot. What are you trying to do to me dad, eh? Do you not care about anyone else apart from yourself? Look at me dad – he's been through hell the last couple of weeks.'

'Oh, and I've been on fucking holiday, have I?'

'I don't give a shit about what you've been through at the moment. Just think about me dad – for Christ's sake, Richard, he's a fucking pensioner.'

Ken rose from his chair. 'Now stop that, David. I don't need you bringing me into this in that way.'

'What the fuck were you doing, Richard?' Stephen joined in. 'You were told by every one of us that they were a bad lot.'

'Oh, and you can fuck off,' said Richard, glaring at Stephen. 'I'll drink with who I want.'

'Just back off, you two,' said Ken. 'It's not his fault. These were his mates – he didn't know what they were up to. Have neither of you ever got involved with people who you later found out were badduns? I know I have.'

'Yeah, Dad, I have,' said David. 'But everybody knew these ones were a bunch of crooks and everybody told him so. He's gone and ruined the family name and he doesn't give a fuck.'

'It'll be sorted,' said Richard, holding on to the arms of his chair.

'Stop acting the fucking hard man,' David shouted. 'You're just playing at this. Why don't you just admit you were wrong?'

'Oh, he won't do that,' Stephen mocked. 'Our Richard admit he was wrong? No chance. Have you any idea what you're putting us all through? My kids are being bullied at school because of this.'

'Why – what's happened?' said Richard, his tone changed.

'What are you going to do? Get one of your gangster mates to beat the kids up that have been teasing my kids? You're a joke.'

'There's no need for that, Stephen,' Ken said.

'Just fuck off home to your wife, Stephen. In fact, why don't you just fuck off altogether? Then you needn't worry about being embarrassed by me.'

Stephen stood up and made for the door. 'I'm out of here,' he yelled back at Richard. 'I'm not stopping to listen to any more shit from him.'

Ken went after him. 'We have to stick together, Stephen,' he told his son in the hallway. 'You have to stand by your brother.'

Stephen looked at his father. 'I don't have to do anything.' He walked out, slamming the door behind him.

Ken felt for the banisters. He sighed as he eased himself down on to the stairs and sat there as he composed himself. The boys were right. Richard had been stupid. But Christ – he was still their brother. They should have been offering him their support no matter how daft he had been.

Richard had tarnished the family name. Even he could see that. But Ken also knew that his son was innocent of the charges laid against him and, whatever mistakes he had made, Richard needed his family united behind him.

When he went back into the room Richard had already left via the back door.

'Shall I get you a fresh brew, Dad?' asked David.

'Why did you say that to the solicitor?'

'Say what?'

'That you thought Richard might run off.'

'Dad – that's not what I said. I just think it's a possibility, and I wanted to know how to protect my money. I still gave the money, didn't I?'

Ken sighed. 'We should be sticking together and thinking about your brother and what he's going through. The money doesn't matter.'

'Of course it bloody matters,' said David. 'It's the money that got him into this mess.'

'What does that mean?' asked Ken.

'If he hadn't had the money and been so hellbent on frittering it away as quickly as possible, he would never have got into drinking with those criminals. He only did it to pass the time when he should have been out grafting.'

'Your brother's grafted hard all his life. He worked day and night on the wagons providing for his family. He deserved a chance to let his hair down.'

'But Christ, Dad. Did he have to be so stupid? Now you're throwing more money at him and this whole mess. How much is this trial going to cost? I know you've told him you'll pay for his defence.'

Ken felt the hairs on the back of his neck bristle. David and Stephen had both taken umbrage when they discovered he was paying for the trial. They wanted Richard to go for legal aid, which was ridiculous. No – his son would be having the best barrister money could buy. It didn't matter how much it cost. It was his duty as a father to do that for Richard.

'That's none of your business,' said Ken coldly.

'But anyway, however much it costs we'll get it all back when he's proved innocent.'

'But it is, Dad. It's *all* our business, because the more money you throw at this trial – if he loses – the less there'll be for our children to inherit.'

'For you to inherit, you mean.'

'No, Dad – for generations to come. At the start you said you wanted this money to set the family up way down the line. If you blow it all now on one member of the family, that just isn't going to happen.'

'I'm not babysitting this money for you and your brothers until I die. When will you start to accept that?'

'That's not –'

'It's not happening. I gave you a million pounds each to do what the hell you wanted with it and I've left you to do it. Now leave me to spend what I kept for myself how the hell I want.'

Stephen could never subscribe to Richard's lifestyle. His ability to spend money appeared to know no bounds, and he was now making a career out of playing the millionaire playboy. He appeared to spend more time out drinking in Manchester than he did with his family. He lived like a single man without responsibilities when Stephen felt he should have been giving more support to his wife and children.

The difference between them was that Stephen enjoyed being a family man. Since the win he had quit work altogether. A million pounds in the bank for him meant an opportunity to spend as much time as possible with Susan and the girls. That was his indulgence.

As a child Stephen had spent little time with his own father, with Ken spending so much time working away from home. He didn't want his own children to have a similarly remote relationship with himself.

Stephen had always been closer to Sheila than to Ken. He had also long been convinced, right or wrong, that Richard was Ken's favourite child. That hurt him deeply. Even now, after having to put up more than a million pounds to get Richard out of prison temporarily at least, their father seemed oblivious to the fact that his little'n had done wrong.

Stephen's happy childhood memories were marred by the blazing rows he often witnessed between his parents. He and Susan had their arguments, but he was confident they maintained more control over what their children saw than his own parents had. Many times he had watched cups and ornaments hurtling across the room as Ken and Sheila launched into yet another tirade against each other. The rows often seemed to be over Ken's movements when he had promised to be at home. Ken would explain that he had been held up for whatever reason, but even as a youngster Stephen had begun to question how anyone could be late on such a regular basis.

He would often find his mother crying to herself when he was a boy and have no idea how to comfort her. She would shrug off her tears, saying she was feeling unwell, and then carry on as normal. At the time he hadn't dwelt too much on why she was upset. There was always plenty going on in his life outside the family to distract him. Now, with hindsight, he guessed that the late nights and missed meals were probably times when his father was out with other women. His mum was probably crying because she knew what was happening but either couldn't or wouldn't do anything about it.

But Stephen could also acknowledge how difficult it must have been for his dad being married to a woman like Sheila. She often lapsed into foul moods and deep depressions and could be hell to live with. He had told her himself in recent years that, had he been married to her, he would have left her long ago. He had to respect his father for standing by her in circumstances he himself would never have tolerated. Perhaps seeking affection elsewhere was the only way his dad could do that.

Stephen's eldest daughter Sarah walked into the study, where he was checking in a newspaper to see how some of his shares were performing. She had been out shopping in town with some of her girlfriends. She kissed him quickly on the cheek before dashing out again to find her mother. It seemed like just a few months ago that she might have climbed on to his knee for a quick cuddle. There was none of that now – she was growing up and felt uncomfortable with too much physical affection from her parents. He could understand that. She was turning into a young woman and had all sorts of emotions to work through.

Physical displays of affection had been pretty much alien to Stephen before he met Susan. His family had never gone in for much hugging and kissing, whereas to Susan these things came as second nature. He liked cuddling his children; it was something he had missed out on himself as a child, something else he felt sad about.

Moving to Australia would help him, he was sure of that. Perhaps, with such a vast physical space between them, he would be able to work through these feelings and then have some kind of relationship with the rest of the Whites. Right now he felt like an outsider.

But he had an idea that if he took control and physically distanced himself from the rest of his family so that he related to them on his own terms then that could change. If it didn't he would be so far away from them all that it wouldn't really matter.

The million pounds Stephen received from his father had been a godsend. He had got into trouble with his VAT returns and owed thousands of pounds. Bad debts against him had not helped. He had been due to meet tax officials just days after the trip to London to get the cheque. His first move when they got home was to arrange to meet the VAT people and wipe out his debt to them.

Even though Ken had given such a large proportion of his lottery money to each of his sons, Stephen was worried about the fact that he was now giving still more of it to Richard.

Ken had paid out a fortune for Richard's and Julie's wedding, buying them expensive gifts to mark the occasion. Now he was prepared to part with every penny he had if it would help keep Richard out of prison. Stephen felt it was another example of ill-placed favouritism.

Stephen saw Richard as a Jekyll and Hyde character. Sometimes he would walk into a room happy and pleasant with everyone in it; at other times he would be in a foul mood and not care whom he upset. On occasions he had sworn at their mother when she had asked him why he was angry. Stephen would immediately berate him for that, and often their father would have to step in to separate them as both their tempers flared.

Stephen had been with Richard the night he met Susan. He was home on leave from the RAF, where he had spent four years as a ground-to-air missile operator. In the event of war his role would have been to shoot down enemy aircraft from the ground.

At the time, he was twenty years old and out on three months' extended leave to prepare him for his return to civilian life. He had been based in Germany and travelled throughout Europe. He turned to the air force after working for his father for a few months after leaving school. He wanted more excitement, which was something he found with the RAF.

That night he and Richard both saw Susan dancing with her friends in the nightclub they had ended up in. They each made a beeline for her, but Stephen got there first. Susan never tired of pointing out to Richard that, had she married him instead of his brother, she would have kept a tighter rein on him than Julie did. Richard was equally quick to point out that he would never have gone as far as marrying her anyway.

Stephen fell for Susan immediately. Not only did he find her exceptionally attractive but he was sure he had found his soul mate. During his time in Europe he had enjoyed plenty of meaningless flings, but he had tired of that way of life.

The following night he took Susan out for a drink. They were the last to leave the pub after talking nonstop about their hopes and dreams for the future. They had met on December the nineteenth; Stephen proposed to her on Boxing Day, exactly a week later. They were married the following April, and their first daughter was born exactly nine months later.

Sheila had been delighted. She took to Susan as instantly as he had, and she remained close to his wife.

His mother was still haunted by the terrible downs that had tarnished her entire life. There were still long periods when she would cut herself off from the world around her. He didn't know how to begin to offer her comfort when she felt that low. But Susan would simply put her arm around her and talk to her so gently, with such love, that Sheila would respond. He would leave them to it, knowing that his wife could reach that part of Sheila that she kept away from everyone else.

His marriage to Susan had always been the most stable, solid thing in Stephen's life. Their courtship might have been brief, but time had shown that their gut feelings about each other were dead right. They were a team. Before the lottery win Stephen would work away driving his wagon long distances while Susan stayed at home with the children. At the weekends he would take over the housework and look after the girls to give her a break. As far as he was concerned, caring for their children was as much his responsibility as hers. He had wanted a large family as much as Susan had, and therefore felt duty-bound to pitch in when he could.

Stephen prided himself on the way he and Susan were so equally matched. She had always been a feisty woman who would not let anyone treat her as anything other than an equal.

After settling his VAT debts, Stephen had gone straight to the building society to pay off his mortgage. As he wrote out the cheque for sixty-five thousand pounds he felt tears of relief well up in his eyes. It was an incredible feeling to know he would never have to worry about meeting his mortgage payments again. He had glanced up at the manager whose office he was sitting in at the time. They shared a smile as he realised this virtual stranger was also filling up with emotion as he witnessed Stephen's joy. He was probably far more used to dealing with people who couldn't afford to meet their monthly payments.

The next few months Stephen spent kicking his heels at home. He wanted to get used to the idea of having so much money before he started to do anything with it. His head had been spinning since the moment his father had told him just how much money he was going to be getting. He needed time to adjust, or he could end up making costly mistakes. As he repeatedly told himself, there were only a thousand thousands in a million. Buying a new house had already taken a chunk out of the money. If it was to set him and his family up for life as he intended, he had to invest it wisely. It was an opportunity given to him by his father that he would be for ever grateful for.

'I'm just off to see Mum,' Stephen called upstairs. Susan was making the beds. 'Dad's got to nip out.'

'Is she all right?' asked Susan, peering down at him from over the landing banisters. They were both concerned about Sheila's health. They had been over to use the pool the day before and she had seemed a little disorientated. She was also unsteady on her feet. Stephen had spent the evening with her when his dad had gone out for a few hours. They had talked about all sorts of things, yet it occurred to Stephen that he couldn't remember exactly what. He enjoyed times like that with his mum. It made him feel close to her.

The doctor had visited her this morning, but his dad hadn't been reassured by anything he had said. His mother never discussed her health with anyone and always put on a brave face however she was feeling. But according to Ken she had been so off-colour that morning that she had barely complained when she saw the doctor had come to examine her.

'Phone me if she seems any worse,' Susan called after him.

When Stephen arrived at his parents' house, Susan, the cleaner, opened the door. She looked flustered.

'What's wrong, Susan? Where's Mum?'

Susan shook her head and led him into the family room where Sheila was sitting on the sofa. She was wearing just her underwear with her dressing gown draped loosely over her shoulders. She was staring straight ahead and seemed unaware of anyone else in the room.

'Mum,' Stephen said gently, walking towards her. 'Mum . . . it's me.'

She didn't look up.

'Where's Dad?' he asked Susan.

'He nipped out when he saw you coming over the road. He wanted to get the prescription the doctor left her.'

Stephen took his mother's hand in his. It felt cold and sticky. He brushed her hair back off her face. She barely noticed his touch. 'Just wait there, Mum. I'm going to get Susan. I won't be long.'

He started to head for the door and then walked back to the telephone. He didn't want to leave Sheila even for the couple of minutes it would have taken to fetch Susan from across the road.

He picked up the telephone and dialled his home number. Susan answered after a couple of rings.

'Can you come over, love? It's Mum.' Susan wanted to know what was wrong. 'I don't know,' he replied. 'She's just not right. I think she needs to see another doctor.'

Stephen hesitated at the door leading into the kitchen and family room. He was dreading seeing his mother in that state again. She looked so distant and out of touch with everything around her. It was as though she had retreated into her own little world, and he doubted if even Susan would be able to pull her out of it.

Chapter Nine

K EN WALKED INTO THE FAMILY ROOM. Sheila was sitting between Stephen and Susan, who each had hold of one of her hands and were rubbing them between their own as if to keep her warm. She was wearing just her underwear, her dressing gown hanging open.

'Sheila, love – are you all right?'

Sheila didn't seem to have heard him. In fact, she didn't seem to be aware he had come into the room. Ken was shocked to see her like that. Sheila had always been such a dignified woman, yet here she was letting her own son see her in her bra and pants. He walked over to her and gently pulled the dressing gown together, covering her up. Sheila didn't seem to realise he was there. Her hands shook as she reached past him for her packet of cigarettes. She kept missing her mouth with the cigarette she had struggled to take out. Her coordination left her completely as she tried to light it, the flame trembling in her hand.

Ken had gone out only to get her prescription from the chemist yet she had deteriorated so much in that short time. He had wanted to go for it earlier, but Susan, their cleaner, had been reluctant to be left alone with Sheila because she looked so unwell. He had had to wait for Stephen and his wife Susan to come over before he could go.

Ken often thought that Sheila felt closer to their cleaner Susan than she did to him. Even at her least communicative she always felt able to talk to her. On the days Susan came to the house Ken would find them together in the kitchen, chatting over a pot of tea. 'I thought we paid Susan to clean the house – not to sit here gassing with you,' he would tease. They just ignored him, returning to their conversation before he left the room. Despite his remarks Ken was glad Sheila had her. Within a year of the win she had begun to lose interest in the new life she had been making for herself. She began to withdraw, gradually spending more of the day in bed. When her mother had died she seemed to give up completely, spending most of her time in Newport with the paperbacks that dominated her life as she grieved. Maggie's death had hit her hard, and she was still reeling from that when Richard was arrested. Susan had become a good friend.

It would never have occurred to Ken to employ a cleaner. The household chores were a part of his life. Weeks after the win the postman had called round to the back of their house in Leigh to deliver a parcel. He had been delighted to see Ken, a multimillionaire, doing his own ironing in the kitchen.

But when they moved, Sheila had asked Susan, who was working for Julie at the time, to come to clean the house on a regular basis.

The first sign that Sheila was ill had come with a thump on the stairs at five o'clock on Saturday morning. She had been up all night reading and watching the evening's television programmes she had taped and fell on the stairs on her way to bed.

When she got up, late that afternoon, Ken asked her what had happened. She seemed unsure, but she said she must have tripped over her dressing gown on the stairs.

On Sunday Sheila had seemed distracted, absent-minded even. Ken was certain she hadn't complained of feeling unwell. She had been popping pills all day, but there was nothing unusual about that. She took painkillers and laxatives by the handful every day. Her mood was no real indication of how she was feeling either. It swung every few hours between a foul temper and sweetness and light. But with hindsight she hadn't been quite herself – that was all he could really be sure of.

Then this morning she had fallen again. She hadn't bothered going to bed at all. At about nine o'clock she had started to get out of her chair and had seemed to lose her balance.

'You don't seem quite right, love,' said Ken, as she composed herself. 'You don't seem to have your balance right.'

'Well, to be honest I don't feel right at all. I can't make out what's going on over there.' She gestured around her. 'Everything just seems such a muddle.'

'I think I need to call the doctor, Sheila. You don't look at all well.'

'Don't you dare call any bloody doctor,' she said, hauling herself to her feet. 'There's nothing wrong with me.'

She walked carefully out of the room and Ken heard the stairs creak as she climbed up to get to the bedroom. He waited until he heard the bedroom door shut and then went to call the doctor.

Ken showed the doctor into the room. Sheila was curled up on the bed.

'Sheila, love, the doctor's here. He wants a quick look at you.'

Sheila turned her head and scowled at them both. But she agreed to let him examine her now he was here.

'You say she doesn't go out much,' he said to Ken as he listened to Sheila's heart.

'No, that's right.' Ken had explained to the receptionist that the doctor would have to come to the house because Sheila wouldn't leave home.

'Sounds to me like agoraphobia.'

'Yes, but I don't think that's what we're here about now.'

The doctor sat on the end of the bed and began to ask Sheila about her symptoms. She was slurring her words and making little sense.'

'You know, you should be getting out more, Mrs White,' he said, taking her hand and gently shaking it.

'Sorry, doctor,' said Ken, 'but it's not the agoraphobia this time. There's something else wrong. What are you going to do about her dizziness? Can you not tell she's not quite herself right now?'

The doctor opened his case and took out his prescription pad. He scribbled on it and tore the page off before handing it to Ken. It was for more painkillers.

Ken and Sheila had left their terrace in Leigh and moved into Twiss Green Farm in the up-market Cheshire town of Culcheth in August 1996. However beautifully renovated their old house had been, it had only two bedrooms so there wasn't enough room for visitors – of which there were many. They agreed they had to find a larger home when, on the night of Richard's and Julie's wedding, Ken had to sleep on the sofa after giving up his bed for guests. It seemed crazy to have millions of pounds in the bank when clearly they needed a bigger house.

They had already bought a rambling seven-bedroomed house for Sheila's mother Maggie in Newport. She had moved into sheltered accommodation but was miserable, away from her family and the community she had lived amongst all her life. Decorating that house had become Sheila's project and she was in her element. For weeks the paperback novels she normally devoured were left alone. Glossy home improvement magazines had replaced them as she looked for ideas for decorating the house.

Twiss Green Farm, a four-bedroomed mock-Tudor house, had just been built when they moved in. Stephen had bought a large house on a new estate behind it soon after the win, and Richard was living with his family in a similar property in the next village. Ken loved the house, with its minstrels' gallery and large, modern rooms. Turning it into a home became his project.

Sheila's total lack of involvement or interest in the move to Culcheth was made clear when, the evening before they left their old house, she went to make a drink and found the kitchen's cupboards bare. She had no idea that Ken had shifted their entire contents to the new house, where everything was already in place.

Leaving Leigh after fourteen years there was a

wrench for Ken. He told few people that they were moving, concerned that his old community would feel he had turned his back on it. But he had grown tired of being a celebrity, with everyone knowing him as Ken White the lottery millionaire. He wanted to be just Ken White again. In Culcheth he could do that. His house was one of many large properties, and some of his neighbours were probably worth more than he was. Wealth was nothing special here, and he saw the move as a chance to start afresh. Ken didn't know if people recognised him or not. If they did, they didn't make any comment; they were more reserved, which meant he felt he had more privacy.

Privacy was something Sheila was desperate for. She had found the constant attention in the early weeks painfully intrusive.

The weekend after the lottery show they had stopped off at Newport market to buy some flowers for her mother, whom they were on their way to visit. The stallholder said he was certain he recognised Ken. Sheila had tensed up instantly and gently pulled on Ken's arm to let him know she wanted them to move on.

'Oh, I grew up around here,' said Ken, as he pointed to the bunch of flowers he wanted. 'It was a long time ago, mind.'

'No, that's not it,' said the flower seller as he shook the water off the stems and wrapped them in paper. 'I've seen you recently.'

Sheila took out her purse and impatiently began to count out the pound coins into his hand. She wanted the conversation to end there.

'I've got it,' he called out as Sheila began to w away. 'You're Ken White, the lottery man off the telly.'

Ken heard Sheila tut and sigh heavily. 'Oh, aye. You saw me on the lottery show then, did you?'

'We'll be late,' Sheila interrupted, scowling at Ken. She began to walk away, tugging on his arm to make it clear he should follow her.

'Bye, then,' Ken called back.

Sheila was furious. 'When the hell am I going to be able to go anywhere with you without people talking to you like that.'

'He meant no harm –'

'I know, I know. But why do you encourage them so much? Why do you have to get into a conversation about it? Can't you think about me for a change? They're not interested in me – I'm just the bloody wife. I have to stand there like an idiot while people treat you like some star.'

'Fine, Sheila – I'll just be rude to people, shall I? I'll just ignore them like you do. If that's what you want, I'll do it.' He quickened his pace, knowing Sheila would have to struggle to keep up.

'Slow down, Ken,' she said, wheezing from the exertion.

He stood still and watched as she struggled to compose herself. She looked tired – he guessed he did too. He walked back towards her and offered her his arm. 'Come on, love. Let's get to your mum's and we'll have a look through some of those holiday brochures. We'll get ourselves on a big ship away from all this and then, when we come back, no one'll be interested in us any more.'

The initial euphoria at winning so much money subsided as the impact it was to have on their everyday lives became apparent. Married life for Ken and Sheila had always been spent with great lengths of time apart because of Ken's work. It was a setup that suited them both.

Now, with Ken no longer working, they were part of each other's lives to an extent they had never known before. At times, each felt as though the other was invading their space, which inevitably led to arguments.

In the ten years leading up to the win, Sheila's body clock had turned upside down. With her family grown up, there was no need for her to fight her desire to stay up all night reading and then sleep through the day. While Ken had occasionally criticised her for it, he was hardly in a position to make too much fuss because he had spent so little time at home. But when Ken won the lottery he stopped work immediately. This threw them together in a way they had never known without any warning and time to prepare for such a change of lifestyle.

At first they merely got under each other's feet and would bicker accordingly. Sheila was still very buoyant and enjoying a renewed interest in life as she threw herself into renovating the seven-bedroomed house they'd bought for her mother. For a time at least, she switched from living as a virtual recluse to darting between their new homes, catching up on friends and family she hadn't even spoken to in a decade or more.

For the first time in his life Ken was faced with endless free time ahead of him. It made him nervous. He was used to snatching holidays when his work allowed. Suddenly he was no longer the breadwinner, striving to keep his family's financial head above water. His role as kingpin within the family – the person they would all come to when they were faced with financial difficulties – appeared redundant. He couldn't see any of them needing to be bailed out of any problems again with so much money behind them.

Minor squabbles developed into resentful battles of wills. Sheila saw it as her right as Ken's wife to give away as much of their money as she saw fit. Previously Ken would give way to Sheila as a matter of course, keeping the little time they spent together peaceful. Now that no longer seemed necessary, and they would row furiously, followed by days of angry silence.

Sheila would argue that she was duty-bound to hand out money to her side of the family. Ken, on the other hand, believed that he had seen his family right by giving three million pounds to their sons. Eventually, Sheila agreed to stop the hand-outs – but not before she had parted with close to a million pounds.

It would take Ken and Sheila many months to settle back into their relationship as each clung to their need to feel in control. Gradually, they learnt to give each other the space they needed by Sheila spending much of her time at her mother's house in Newport while Ken remained in the new house in Culcheth.

In July 1995 Ken finally realised his ultimate ambition when he booked them a first-class cabin on a ship cruising along the Rhine. They took with them Ken's sister Mavis and her husband Len and Sheila's sister Elaine and husband Geoff.

Their guests also travelled first class, with Ken

footing the bill for them all. It was generally presumed that he would do this, and there were no awkward moments when bills had to be paid. He had always been a generous man and never flinched from picking up the tab for his relatives if he had the cash to do so.

Being away from home helped Ken appreciate just how much of an effect the money was having on them. Sitting on the deck of the massive liner, watching the water being forced aside as she smashed a path through it, Ken experienced a feeling of normality he hadn't realised was missing from his life.

Even though he was doing something out of the ordinary, something he had hoped to do all his life, he was sharing the experience with many other people. His fellow passengers came from all walks of life. Some were wealthy, the trip just another holiday for them; others would have saved hard, perhaps all their lives, for these few weeks' cruise. But however any of them, including himself, had got here didn't matter. The very fact they were there meant they had something in common.

Winning the lottery was an isolating experience by the mere fact that so few people had done it. The lottery and the wealth it had given them had dominated his life, his thoughts and his plans from the day he won. He had remained the same person he was before, and that was proving the hardest thing of all. He looked the same and felt the same. Only everything around him was different.

It was wonderful to be doing something else, something he knew he would have achieved some day whether he had won his millions or not. The day would have come when he would have saved the money to do it, without a family crisis to then wipe it out. Ironically, while many of the passengers on board had chosen a cruise to get away from the rest of the world, being here made Ken feel a part of it again.

Ken spent much of his time out on deck pondering on how his life had changed. People would smile at him as they walked past, as though they were acknowledging that the place where he sat had become his own small piece of the ship.

Sheila was happiest in their cabin, sleeping or reading, although she did join them on some of their trips ashore. First stop was Amsterdam, and it was there that Ken found a small jeweller's shop with a tray of diamond pendants in the window.

'I still owe you a necklace to make up for that piece of tat the lottery girl picked up for me,' Ken told Sheila as they looked over the display. A pretty diamond-studded cross had caught his eye. 'Will you let me choose one of these for you?'

Ken had always taken great pleasure from picking out pieces of jewellery for his wife, and she had never been disappointed with his choices. Sheila nodded and smiled. She waited outside as he went into the shop.

He rejoined her a few minutes later, the chain and cross held tightly in his right hand. He had told the shop assistant not to wrap it – he wanted his wife to wear it straight away.

'Close your eyes, love,' he said, moving behind her. 'I'll just fasten it on for you.'

'You daft sod,' said Sheila. But she did as he asked. 'Aren't we a bit old for this kind of thing?' she teased him.

Ken clicked the clasp shut and turned her around to face him.

'That looks fine. Here – take a look for yourself.' He guided her to admire the piece in the shop window.

Sheila felt the heavy chain and pendant in her hand and smiled at her reflection. 'It's lovely, Ken, just lovely. Thank you.'

She held out her hand and he took it in his. Then they walked together towards the coffee shop where they had arranged to meet up with the others.

'It'll always be special, this necklace,' said Sheila quietly. 'I'll always think of this as being the first thing you bought me with the money.'

'Are you happy, Sheila – are you glad we came away?'

'Oh, yes. Very.'

'We'll do this again, won't we – go on other cruises, I mean?'

'Yes, I think so.'

Ken squeezed her hand in his. He didn't care if Sheila spent the rest of this and every other cruise he planned for them in her cabin reading her books. This was clearly the best way for them to travel. She could escape to their room whenever she needed to, while he could sail on the world's oceans in style. This was how he wanted them to spend the rest of their lives together.

The Rhine cruise was the first of many Ken and Sheila enjoyed together. They travelled across much of the world during the next two years as they discovered however much tension there was at home this was their way of escaping. It kept them happy to be together.

*   *   *

'I'll take her up to bed,' said Ken. He and Stephen helped her to her feet.

'I'll call the doctor – and I'll make sure it's a different one this time,' said Susan.

Sheila seemed oblivious to the conversations going on around her as they guided her into bed. Ken plumped up the pillow before easing Sheila's head back down on to it. The back of her neck felt clammy.

The bedroom door opened. It was Susan with the doctor. Sheila looked at her daughter-in-law for reassurance – she was the only one of them she seemed to recognise.

'It's all right, Mum,' said Susan gently. 'The doctor just needs a quick look at you.'

They left the room while the doctor examined her. However disorientated Sheila might be, there was no way she would want an audience for that. He joined them on the landing outside the room a few minutes later.

'I'm calling an ambulance,' he said calmly. 'She's got a very high temperature – she needs to be in hospital.'

'There's no need for that,' said Ken. 'I've got my car outside. We can take her to a private hospital ourselves.'

'Take her yourselves by all means. But she needs to go to Warrington General. They're going to have to run some tests, and they've all the facilities there. Think about a private hospital when we know what's wrong with her.'

'I'll get her down then,' said Susan. 'We won't be long. You get the car ready.'

Ken stood at the bottom of the stairs as Susan and

Stephen gently guided Sheila down. She looked frightened, totally dependent on the two people at either side of her. Sheila was such a feisty, independent, pain in the neck of a woman most of the time. Weakness wasn't a part of her make-up. Stephen was close to tears – it was clearly torturous for him to see the mother he adored so weak. Susan, who was also very close to Sheila, was hiding her emotions well. She was a strong woman and Ken knew that both he and his son would be able to lean on her physically and emotionally for as long as they needed to. Not that they would need to for long. The doctor had said he thought she had some kind of infection. A blast of antibiotics at the hospital would soon see her right.

They drove to the hospital in silence. Sheila had been upset when Ken explained where they were going.

'You're going to be in the best place. Then, when they know what's wrong, I'll have you moved to a nice private hospital.'

She hadn't spoken since. Now she was behind some curtains in a bed on a main ward while the doctors tried to find out what was wrong.

They quickly discovered she had a blood clot that was moving around her body. They just didn't know how much damage it had caused.

But more urgent than that was treating her for the pneumonia they knew was wreaking havoc on her body. They needed to control that before they could begin to deal with the blood clot.

'Her lungs are filling with fluid, and our immediate concern is getting them clear,' the doctor explained to them in a side room. 'The problem is they are filling up again faster than we are draining them. I'm sorry, Mr White, but we've got a battle on our hands here.'

The room juddered as Ken struggled for words. 'Will she be all right, then?' was all he could think to say.

'We're doing everything we can.'

'Well, can I move her to a private hospital, then?'

'Not now. They don't have the facilities needed to treat your wife. She has to stay here if we want to get her better.'

Ken pulled a chair up to the bed where Sheila lay and sat down. She had a monitor clipped on to one of her fingers and a drip into the back of her hand. Other wires and tubes were attached to her chest. She appeared to be sedated and was drifting in and out of consciousness. Every so often, even in her sleep, she would pull at the wires attached to her, sometimes disconnecting them. That would trigger an alarm, alerting the nurse to rush over and replace whatever she had pulled out.

Stephen had gone to ring his brothers to let them know what had happened. Susan was talking to a doctor at the ward door. Thank God she was here. She seemed to be able to detach herself from how she must be feeling and stay calm.

Sheila stirred and moaned quietly. Ken grabbed her hand. It felt cold, while the rest of her body was hot and sticky.

'What a fright you're giving us here, love,' said Ken, surprised by how much his voice trembled as he spoke. He took a handkerchief out of his trouser pocket and wiped at his eyes, just in case. He glanced around the other beds but didn't even notice the people in them. He just wished they had more privacy.

'Now then, Sheila, how are you feeling?' Susan asked as she joined him at the bedside. Sheila stirred and pulled the clip off her finger. The nurse came running over to put it back on.

'This is ridiculous,' Susan said to her as she reset the monitor. 'She needs someone with her all the time. You've got all these other people to worry about as well.'

'It's all right. I'm used to it.' The nurse bustled off in the direction of one of the other beds, where an elderly woman was calling out for her.

'Sheila, you've got to stop pulling at these monitors. They're there for your own good,' Ken scolded her. She mumbled incoherently.

Stephen returned. 'They're on their way.' His eyes were red and his face was covered in blotches. He didn't take his eyes off his mother. 'God – she'd better be all right.'

'She will, lad, she will. She's a fighter, your mum. You've got to think positive.'

David and Richard arrived together.

'What do they say – the doctors, what do they think?' David asked urgently.

Ken brought his sons up to date with the situation.

'Did anyone know she was ill?' said Richard. 'I had no idea there was anything wrong with her.'

'None of you knew, son. You know your mother – she only tells you what she wants you to know.' Sheila stirred again. 'Isn't that right, love?'

'Eh?' she mumbled.

'I said you only tell us what you want us to know.'

Sheila didn't answer. She seemed to be asleep again.

That night Ken hardly slept. He was certain Sheila would be fine, but he knew they had some tough days ahead. The doctors seemed very concerned, but then they always prepare you for the worst. They have to cover themselves, he guessed.

What really upset Ken was the way Sheila was behaving and the speed at which she had deteriorated. The image of her sitting there, half-dressed, would haunt him for a long time. She would normally have been devastated should one of her sons see her like that, yet she hadn't even been aware that her beloved Stephen was even in the room. Her mind was so confused. He prayed it wouldn't be a permanent aftereffect of this damned blood clot.

The following morning Ken braced himself before entering the ward. He advised Stephen to do the same. 'She probably won't seem herself for a while yet. We need to be strong for her.'

Ken caught his breath as he walked towards the bed where he had left his wife, barely conscious, the night before.

Sheila was sitting up chatting with the woman in the next bed. 'Here they are,' she told her as she caught sight of them. 'That's Stephen, my middle lad, and his wife Susan. And that's my husband Ken.'

The three looked at each other in amazement. It was hard to believe they had left her so poorly, yet she seemed so well today.

'How are you today, love? You look a lot better,' said Ken, leaning over to kiss her on the cheek.

'Oh, Mum, you do look better. We've been so worried about you.'

'Oh, don't you worry about me. There's some women in here who are really poorly. I'll be fine.' She began to tell them about her fellow patients and relayed what the doctors had told her was happening to her own body. 'They need to do some more tests, but I'll soon be back on my feet,' she reassured them.

Later that morning, after David and Richard had arrived, Sheila's consultant came over to talk to them. 'We still need to get her scanned,' he explained. 'But we haven't got the pneumonia under control yet.'

'Can we not get her into a side ward?' asked David. Sheila was still fiddling with the wires attached to her body and every so often would pull another one loose. 'She needs her own nurse to make sure she keeps all the drips and things attached.'

The consultant explained that they simply didn't have the resources.

'Well, then, I'll pay for her to have a nurse and her own room. Money isn't a problem for us.'

Eventually, one of the hospital managers was brought down to speak to Ken. He agreed that they could hire their own nurse from an agency to sit with her round the clock in a private room.

As the day went on, Sheila's condition began to deteriorate again. She started to slur her words and seemed to forget where she was or who was with her.

'I'm not happy with this, Dad,' said David. 'She should be in intensive care. They're as worried about her as we are, so why aren't they doing any more for her?'

'You go and talk to them, lad. See what they can do.'

He came back a few minutes later, his face red.

'They haven't got the bloody beds or nurses up there to move her. Apparently there's people here more poorly than she is. It's fucking ridiculous.'

The next morning Sheila was totally incoherent, and when she was awake she stared at her family blankly.

'She doesn't even know we're here,' said David. 'She needs to be in intensive care. What the hell are they playing at?' He marched out of the room to find a doctor.

The doctor came in to explain the situation. 'Yes, she does need intensive care,' he said. 'But we just haven't got a bed for her yet. We've got someone ringing round all the hospitals in the area to see if they can take her. As soon as one comes available, it's hers.'

They began to take it in turns to ask a member of the medical team whether a bed in intensive care was ready for her. Finally, on Thursday morning, there was.

It was now clear that Sheila was desperately ill. Not only were the doctors fighting to keep her lungs clear, but they had now discovered that septicaemia was poisoning her body.

'We're fighting an uphill battle,' the consultant explained. 'I'll be honest. The only time I've ever known septicaemia spread through a body so fast is in an AIDS victim. It's as though her immune system is shot through.'

Ken thought of all the tablets Sheila had swallowed during her lifetime. She hadn't been to the lavatory naturally in years – she took laxatives like they were sweets. She was the same with painkillers, and everyone knew she had chain-smoked all her adult life.

'She must have known,' said Ken, turning to David. 'She must have known from her nursing that something was wrong. She could have been ill for years, but she would have been too stubborn to tell us or do anything about it.'

'Don't give up yet, Dad,' said Richard, placing his hand on his father's arm.

'He's right, Dad,' added David. 'At least they've got her in the right place now.'

'I'm not giving up on her,' said Ken angrily. 'When have I ever given up on any of you? I'm just trying to think how this could have happened.'

They all took it in turns to sit with Sheila, who was heavily sedated. The rest of the family, joined now by Julie and Lynne, waited in the corridor outside until it was their turn.

Ken was finding difficulty in containing his anger at the doctors, who he felt had delayed in getting Sheila the treatment she needed. David was the same. Ken was furious with the GP who had first seen Sheila at the house and had dismissed her symptoms as being part of the agoraphobia that had blighted her life. He couldn't help but think that if he had acted as quickly as his colleague Sheila would never have got so ill.

'Why didn't you just move another bed in here for her instead of waiting so long?' Ken demanded.

'It's not that easy, Mr White. You need specially trained nurses to go with that bed.'

'Let it go for now, Dad,' said David wearily. They both knew this was not the time to cause a row. That could wait until Sheila was better.

Sheila's condition improved and deteriorated throughout that day, but by late evening she seemed to be improving again.

One of the nurses took Ken to one side. 'Why don't you take your family home so you can all get some sleep? She's not too bad at the moment, and you know we'll call you if you're needed here.'

'No, no. She needs me here. How could I sleep anyway?'

'Well, just get some rest and a proper hot meal inside you,' she insisted.

David appeared. 'Go on, Dad. I'll stay with Mum. You go and get some rest. You're no good to her if you get ill too.'

Ken was still awake when the telephone rang. He looked at the bedside clock as he picked up the receiver. It was just after 1 a.m.

'Dad – it's Richard. They need us at the hospital. I'll pick you up in five minutes.'

'Right, then,' said Ken. He didn't want to know why they were needed. Somehow he had managed to shut off the part of his brain that wanted to ask questions. That way he didn't have to deal with the answers. He knew enough by the very fact that they wanted him back. They were hardly going to call him out in the middle of the night to tell him she was getting better.

Incredibly, Sheila had pulled through that crisis by the time they arrived and her condition was stable again. Ken returned home to try to snatch a few hours' sleep before morning. By now he was too tired to argue with the nurse when she told him to go. He felt light-headed with exhaustion and found himself close to tears when he looked at his wife. He needed a break.

The next morning he was again at Sheila's bedside with Julie.

'She looks very peaceful – not at all uncomfortable,' said Julie, brushing Sheila's hair back off her face. 'They always say that sleep is the best medicine.'

The boys joined them. 'I'll take over now,' said Stephen. 'You go and get yourselves a cup of tea or something.'

Ken looked at his sons. They all looked shattered – emotionally and physically. 'I'm all right here for a bit,' he said.

'Mr White?' It was the consultant. No one had noticed him as he approached the bed.

Ken looked at him and smiled. 'How's she doing, then? A bit better this morning, is she?'

'Mr White, can I just have a quiet word?' He motioned to a side room and began to walk to it. Ken stood up slowly and smiled across at his family before following him into it. He pulled out a chair for Ken to sit on and then another for himself. Then he cleared his throat.

'As you know, we've been treating your wife with the best drugs we have for her condition. We are giving her those drugs at the highest potency we can, but her lungs are filling up so fast now we cannot keep them clear. You've seen the machine – the ventilator – that she's attached to?'

Ken nodded, his eyes firmly fixed on the consultant's face.

'That's making her breathe. It's squeezing her lungs for her. You can see her chest rising and falling, and it must look as though she's breathing naturally. But she isn't.'

Ken nodded again.

'We can't save her, Mr White. We're going to have

to switch that ventilator off, and when we do your wife will die.'

Later, Ken would feel deep gratitude towards that consultant for the way in which he explained that Sheila was going to die. He phrased his explanation so that there was no decision for Ken to make. The doctor had decided for him that Sheila couldn't go on, and Ken knew that he was right. There was no deliberating – no guilt for him to have to deal with. All he could do now was to be there as she slipped away.

The family waited outside as the nursing staff switched off the machine and removed the wires from Sheila's body. Nobody spoke. It didn't even feel right to cry at that point because, as the doctor had explained, she wouldn't die straight away.

They returned to her bed, where chairs had been arranged around it for them to sit on.

Ken was the first to speak. 'Well, Sheila, are you comfortable, love? You look better without those blasted wires all over . . .' He began to weep quietly, hiding his eyes beneath his hands. The one monitor left showed her heart rate. He guessed that would stop when she died.

But that was as far ahead as he could see. All his life, every difficult situation he encountered, he had looked forward to see what his next move should be, or what the people around him would do next. Right now the only prediction he could make was that Sheila wouldn't be coming home with him.

He had millions of pounds in the bank, yet right now his money had no value to him whatsoever. What was the good of all that money if it couldn't save the woman he loved? And by God he loved Sheila. No matter how angry and bitter they were towards each other at times, they had been together all their adult lives.

He became aware of his sons and their wives each speaking in turn to her. He couldn't hear what they were saying – their voices were drowned out by Sheila's as he imagined her talking to him just one more time.

The steady pulse of the machine became hypnotic as Ken stared at the woman he had shared the last forty-odd years with. He felt strangely detached from the whole miserable scene, yet he knew that in minutes or hours from now he would be grieving the loss of the biggest part of his life.

Suddenly the machine stopped beating, and the pulse turned into a high-pitched wail. Ken's eyes darted to the monitor, as did everyone else's. Where before the trace had been rising and falling, now it was a long flat line. She had gone.

Ken gasped and then let out a deep moan. This was it – she looked the same. Still, as though she was sleeping.

He was holding her hand and now placed his other over them both, desperately clinging on to the warmth that would soon leave her. Then he began to cry. Quietly at first, then louder as he forced himself to accept that she had gone.

Around him his children wept, their wives unable to comfort them as they, too, cried for Sheila. It had taken less than an hour from when they switched off the machine.

Chapter Ten

RICHARD STOOD AT THE CEMETERY GATES waiting for his father. Autumn had arrived and it was getting cold. He stamped his feet to keep warm and pulled his coat around him. The others were waiting in the cars ready to go back to the house, where Susan had organised food and drinks for the mourners. Ken walked slowly towards his son. He had wanted a few moments alone with Sheila at the graveside to say his own goodbyes.

'It's a lovely spot you've got her, Dad,' said Richard as Ken reached him. 'It's really beautiful.'

Ken nodded. 'I've just been thinking that. I'll be joining her here myself one day.' He began to cry.

'Come on, Dad. Let's get you in the warm. We'll go home now and give her a good sendoff.'

Sheila had always said that when she died she wanted her funeral to be in Wales. Ken had often teased her about it, saying that once she was gone he would decide where she would be buried and that she wouldn't be around to argue about it.

But after her death Ken had reached a compromise. He had arranged for a special service and cremation to be held in Newport. Then her ashes were brought home and placed in a plot in a private cemetery in Worsley, just outside Manchester.

Ken had bought the plot at Woodlands a few months before Sheila died, believing at the time that it would be for himself. He had never imagined that his wife would die before him.

He had arranged for a willow tree to be planted there for her and a bench beside it where he and his sons would be able to sit when they visited her. The gravestone, which, in line with the cemetery rules, had to lie flat, was heart-shaped and surrounded with vases for flowers. Sheila's name was on one side; the other was left empty for Ken's when he finally joined her there.

As they reached the car Richard looked back towards the cemetery. 'She'll never know now.'

'Know what, lad?'

'What happens with this trial. I know she had her doubts that I'd get off. I hate the thought of her never knowing what happens.'

'She'll know, son. She'll have a big smile on her face the day you leave that court a free man. You don't need to worry about that.'

They moved around to the side of the car.

'It was probably the best thing for her, to go the way she did,' said Richard. 'She would have hated it if she'd pulled through and ended up paralysed or something from that blood clot.'

'Aye, she would. It wouldn't have been your mother – dependent on the rest of us.'

They stood together in silence for a moment, the crisp, cold air biting at their faces.

'Come on, son – it's time to go. We can come back and see her any time we want now.'

* * *

Living alone in the house in Culcheth was less of an ordeal than Ken had expected. Sheila had spent little time there, and it had been decorated to his tastes. There were few reminders of his wife – even the ornaments were mostly pieces he had chosen himself. Visiting the house in Newport, however, was something he would put off for many months because it had become so much a part of Sheila.

Susan remained the rock that Ken had predicted she would be. She sorted through all of Sheila's personal effects and arranged for her clothes to be given to charity. Perhaps the hardest task for Ken was sorting through her jewellery. He had bought her pieces from all over the world on his travels with his work. The trinkets he bought her before the win were of little monetary value compared with those he bought her after. But each one reminded him of a moment they had shared.

He had told his daughters-in-law to each choose a ring after Sheila's funeral to remember her by. Now, he wanted to choose some pieces to give to his granddaughters before placing the rest at the bank.

The gold cross they'd bought together in Amsterdam caught his eye. He brushed away a tear as he remembered how pleased Sheila had been when he'd placed it around her neck. He would give that to Helena, his eldest grandchild and David's eldest daughter. She was old enough to appreciate what it had meant to them. The rest he put aside as gifts he would make to the girls as they grew up. He gave no thought to how valuable each item was – he simply chose the ones he thought were the prettiest.

Sheila's death had temporarily reunited Stephen and Ken after a bitter argument they'd had shortly before she'd been taken ill. Stephen had gone with his family to Australia with the intention of settling there, but they'd returned after failing to find a business they wanted to invest in. While they were out there Stephen had paid a deposit on a piece of land in Brisbane to build a house on. He had then presumed that when he decided to return to England the landowner would keep the deposit as recompense for the lost sale.

Instead, he pursued Stephen back to England for the money. To avoid litigation, Stephen needed to find forty-two thousand pounds quickly to complete the sale. But all his cash was tied up in property and shares, and it would take time to release that amount.

Ken stepped in and paid for the land, and for months there was no mention of the matter. The land remained in Stephen's name, although technically Ken owned it. Later Ken had made enquiries about it through Stephen's solicitor with a view to selling it.

Stephen discovered what Ken had been doing when a fax came through to his own house about the matter. He had been furious and went straight round to his father's house to confront him. A nasty row followed which left them both smarting. For the first time Ken could remember, Sheila had sided with him, angered by the way Stephen had spoken to him.

The whole matter had left both of them bitter and it remained an underlying source of resentment that was never truly resolved because of Sheila's death.

But the greatest source of conflict within the family had come months earlier when news of Richard's arrest came through. Ken and Sheila were in South Wales with Maggie when Julie called to tell them what had happened. Ken was about to leave the house to go to his brother Les's funeral when he took the phone call. Susan was with them – she and Sheila were going to spend a few days there before returning to Cheshire.

Sheila was furious when Ken told her what he knew. 'What trouble has he got himself into now?' she'd yelled. 'Christ, Ken – how many times did he need telling that he was getting in with a bad lot? He's brought shame on this family.'

'Hold on, hold on,' said Ken. 'We don't know the ins and outs yet. Don't start shouting the place down until we know what's happened.'

'Don't start shouting? That's a joke. Maybe if you'd done a bit more shouting with that one instead of letting him get away with murder he wouldn't be in this mess now.'

'Just leave it for now, Sheila,' Ken had told her. 'We've got to bury my brother yet.'

Les, who was born on the same day as Ken only eighteen years earlier, had been ill for more than a year and his death had been expected. With such a large age gap the brothers had not been particularly close, but Ken had done what he could to make his final months as pleasant as possible. He had paid for holidays for him and his wife Sylvia and had bought them new furniture and carpets.

'You're not going to tell anyone what's happened, are you?' Sheila had asked.

'What do you take me for, woman? Of course I'm not. With any luck this whole thing'll blow over and no one will ever have to know.'

Ken went to the funeral and then back to his sister-in-law's house.

'Sylv, I'm going to have to get straight off now. I've some business to deal with at home,' he explained.

Sylvia began to cry. 'I just don't know how I'm going to pay for all this,' she sobbed. 'This funeral business, it's so expensive.'

'Oh, just send me the bill,' Ken snapped. He was used to Sylvia dropping hints about what she needed, but on this day he had little patience with her. 'Send me all the bills and I'll pay for the bloody lot.'

Susan had then returned to Cheshire with Ken while Sheila stayed in North Wales.

Christmas without Sheila was harder than Ken could ever have imagined. When she had been alive they had always spent the day quietly at home, with the children and grandchildren calling over in the afternoon.

This year, and this day more than any other, brought home to Ken how much he missed his wife. It also showed him what a huge part of his life she had been even though they had spent so much time apart. For the first time since her death he felt truly on his own instead of part of a couple, no matter how distant the marriage might sometimes have been.

He went to bed on Christmas Eve feeling positive about the day ahead. He told himself that it was just another day that lay ahead, and that he didn't even need to think about the fact that it was Christmas until he went round to Stephen's house for his lunch. Then he would get into the spirit of things for the children's sake.

When he awoke his first thoughts were for Sheila.

It wasn't as though she was that bothered about Christmas – it was just a day to spend time with the family to her. But today he would be spending time with the family without her, and he felt sad at the prospect.

The lunch at Stephen's house was an enjoyable distraction. In the afternoon the rest of his family called in to see him. It wasn't until the evening that Ken truly appreciated how empty he felt not having Sheila around.

They had never been great talkers or done anything together as a couple. They had little in common except for a fierce love for their children. But she had been a part of him for forty-five years and now she was gone. He felt older than he was and lonelier than he had ever imagined he could be. What made it worse was that he could see nothing beyond how he felt at that moment except many more Christmases alone. His grief felt more real than it had at any point since October when she died. He was alone – and nothing was ever going to change that.

In January the date for Richard's trial came through. Some of his co-accused had already pleaded guilty. He would be appearing in April at Manchester Crown Court with the other two who were proclaiming their innocence.

Stephen would not be in the country for the trial. He and his family had decided to emigrate to Australia – for good, this time. Stephen didn't want his family to be subjected to more bad publicity. His children had been through a tough time at school over the court case, and he felt it was better for them not to be around.

Ken could understand them wanting to get away. But surely they could have taken a long holiday and come back when the thing was finished? He was unhappy with the way the children were being uprooted again. They had already tried it out there once and come back. Why was it going to work any better this time?

His relationship with Stephen had deteriorated again since Richard's arrest. Like David, Stephen was unhappy with the amount of money Ken was throwing at the trial. There had also been quarrels between the three of them over Ken putting money offshore to protect it from inheritance tax if he should die. Sheila's death had brought their own mortality home to all of them. It also left Ken's money more vulnerable to the tax man, which Stephen and David were quick to point out.

At one point it had even been suggested that Ken should put all his funds into his sons' names; they could then give him money as and when he needed it. Ken had been horrified by this and resisted strongly. He told them that he felt as though they simply wanted to mind his money for him until he died.

Stephen and Susan left for the airport at six o'clock in the morning. Their house sold and their furniture already on its way to Australia, they had moved in with Ken for a few days before they left the country. The atmosphere had been tense, and there was little affection shown as they said goodbye.

Ken had planned to hold a small farewell party for them the weekend before they left. Stephen and Susan had refused, saying they wanted to go out with their friends instead. Ken had snapped: 'It's not your friends you should be thinking about – it's your bloody family. If you get into a mess out there it'll be your family you'll come to for help, not your friends.'

But this morning Ken was most concerned about his granddaughters, who had looked weary even before they set out on a gruelling journey to the other side of the world. He wondered when he would see them again.

In the months that followed there was to be little contact between Ken and Stephen, except for the occasional phone call, a situation that hurt them both deeply yet neither seemed prepared to do anything to change it.

Ken walked back into the house, the taxi taking them to the airport out of sight. He went into the family room and looked to Sheila's chair. He could picture her now, fag in one hand and a paperback in the other, with her feet tucked under her.

He lowered himself heavily into his own chair, still staring at the one where he wife once sat.

'It's been another bleedin' day, love. Another bleedin' day.'

He carried on talking, imagining Sheila was there with him only half-listening to what he had to say. 'Did I do this all wrong, Sheila? Did I make a mistake giving them all that money?'

He was beginning to think he might have. Since the win, at times he thought David and Stephen had turned greedy. Surely if he had nothing left for them by the time he died, that shouldn't matter. It was up to him what he did with his money.

The idea that he should sign the money over to them and ask them for pocket money was a joke.

There was no way he wanted his children scrutinising what he was spending his money on.

Ken walked through the conservatory and picked up a photograph of Sheila from the coffee table. He carried it into the pool-house with him. This was his favourite place. He'd had it built entirely to his own specifications and there was a gym and sauna alongside it. The air was warm and sticky in here. He loved the way it hit you as you walked through the doors. It was like this all day and night because he kept the heating on.

'They wouldn't have liked handing me cheques to pay for building this, would they, Sheila?' he said, looking at the photograph in his hand.

Ken laughed. There had been raised eyebrows enough over the amount of money he had spent on it. It had gone thirty thousand over budget and ended up costing over a hundred thousand. He didn't care how much it had cost – it was one thing he really wanted to do. Meanwhile, Richard was on trial for drug smuggling and had spent the last two years of his life on a drinking and spending binge.

With hindsight Ken wondered if he should have staggered the money and given it to his sons in instalments. Maybe they would have handled it better? But he could never have known this would happen.

'I thought they were mature enough to handle it, love. Maybe I was wrong.'

But no – he didn't really think he had been wrong. They were just handling it in their own ways. Things would settle down in time. The money had just brought a few issues out into the open that had been bubbling beneath the surface anyway, he told himself.

'Families argue, don't they, Sheila?' They especially rowed about money, he thought, which was something the Whites had more of than most. It was still early days – they had plenty of time to get used to the money.

Ken turned back into the conservatory then through the family room into the kitchen. He turned on the tap and began to fill the kettle.

'The trial starts next month, Sheila,' he called back. 'Then we can stop worrying about what's going to happen to the little'n because this stupid mess'll be sorted out.'

Chapter Eleven

STEPHEN'S STOMACH LURCHED as the taxi pulled on to the motorway heading for Manchester Airport. It was a journey they had made many times before as they flew off on family holidays. He glanced back at his children. They looked tired and thoughtful. He guessed they were reflecting on the life they were leaving behind. This had to be even harder for them than it was for him and Susan.

The atmosphere as they left his father's house had been tense. Stephen had barely looked at Ken as they got into the car. There was so much sorrow over the deterioration of his relationship with Ken that he had found it impossible to put on any show of affection even though he knew he might never see him again.

The airport lights came into view. Stephen wondered if his father would even notice they had gone. He doubted it. Ken had shown little interest in him and his family – now he would have even less cause to.

His dad probably wouldn't even have worked out why things had deteriorated so spectacularly between them in the last few months. He wasn't about to tell him. Maybe in time he would work it out for himself.

* * *

Stephen had always felt second best to Richard where his father was concerned. As a child he would burn with jealousy as he watched Ken lavish love and attention on his younger brother. Even a trip out to buy shoes would make him feel let down. He was convinced that his father begrudged paying out for new shoes for himself yet delighted in buying Richard the most expensive pair in the shop.

It was to his mother that Stephen turned for love – something she seemed to give him gladly. After the lottery win it was also Sheila whom Stephen relied on to make sure he and his family were treated as well as his younger brother's. She would point out to Ken that, if he paid, say, school fees for Richard's children, he should do something similar for the rest of his grandchildren.

At Christmas and birthdays she would make sure the children had a gift off their grandparents – something to show that some thought had gone into what they received. This Christmas they had each opened the cards to find a hundred pounds inside. It might have been a lot of money to them all, but Stephen was certain a proper gift would have meant more to them.

The end for Stephen came at his mother's funeral wake back at the house. He had been devastated when, at the service before the burial, he saw among the mourners people his father had invited whom they all knew his mother had little time for. Stephen felt that Ken had betrayed Sheila and her memory by allowing people to mourn her whom he saw as nothing more than hangers-on. It was as though the whole event had been turned into some kind of social gathering. He felt it was wrong.

He and Susan went back to their own house after the funeral, unable to mingle with people in Sheila's old house who they knew had she been alive would never have got through the front door.

Stephen handed his travel papers over at the check-in desk. They still had a good couple of hours before their flight. Susan had taken the children through to the restaurant to get some breakfast. They hadn't felt much like eating back at the house before they left. He walked away from the row of desks and glanced back in time to see their suitcases being carried off on the escalator to take them on to their plane. The next time he would see them would be at the airport in Australia.

Over at the departure gates a family was saying their goodbyes to some friends or relatives who had come to see them off. He felt a pang of sadness as he thought of his own father back at the house in Culcheth. He considered calling him. Maybe they didn't have to part so badly after all? But he couldn't do it. It was time to break away.

He spotted Susan and the girls at a table near the window of the restaurant. They were looking out at the aeroplanes, Nikki, his youngest, squealing with delight as they took off. This was his family, the woman he loved, who had loved him throughout seventeen years of marriage, and his precious children. They would start a new life together and leave all the bitterness and wrangling over money behind them.

In Australia no one would be interested in how much money they had – and, more important, how they had got it. Stephen certainly wouldn't be volunteering the information. He planned to rent for the first few months until they found their feet. Then they would build themselves a house for around a hundred and fifty thousand pounds. Judging by standards of living out there that would be pretty average – their neighbours would expect them to be mortgaged up to the hilt to pay for it. Instead, they would be buying it outright.

Stephen intended never to be in debt again. From now on his home and cars would be paid for in cash as a kind of security blanket in case everything else went pear-shaped. More than that, he had also vowed never to spend money on anything that wasn't a necessity. They would live off the income generated by investments – but whatever luxuries they wanted from now on had to be earned.

David, who was also careful with his money, had found this amusing. He had laughed when Stephen had told him that he planned to buy himself a sports car within the next five years. 'Buy it now,' he had said. 'It's not like you can't afford it.'

But Stephen saw it differently. He was now utterly convinced that his father would not be leaving any form of inheritance for him and his children. He was sure that Richard would spend his way through whatever Ken had left.

Even if he didn't, Stephen was certain his dad would have written him out of any will he had made. That didn't matter to Stephen any more. He didn't want to be dependent on a payout when his father died – he didn't want that to be the basis of his relationship with Ken.

Since getting the money each member of the family had indulged themselves in one way or another.

David had bought himself a flashy sports car, Richard had gone on a two-year spending spree and Ken spent his time travelling the world on cruise ships. Stephen's indulgence was his family – taking time out from the rat race to be at home with Susan and the girls.

Now he was ready to work again. Stocks and shares had always fascinated him – when he was driving wagons he would play fantasy share-dealing in his cab. Each week he would pick out some companies and imagine he had bought shares in them. He would then follow their fortunes as though he had actually invested in them, scribbling the outcome down in a notebook. He discovered he was quite good at it.

Now, he had the money to do it properly and was making a good profit. It was a way of working from home, doing something he enjoyed and adding to the family's wealth. He invested only in safe bets but was doing well, making hundreds of pounds' profit each week. He would do the same in Australia.

A major cause for dispute between Stephen and his father had come soon after Sheila's death when he and David had urged Ken to put most of his money offshore. That way there would be a legacy left for future generations of the White family. Doing so would have protected the money from Richard and even from Ken, who, as far as they were concerned, sometimes spent his money unwisely. If it was out of his reach he couldn't be conned into giving it to the many people who went to him with projects for him to invest in. On reflection Stephen could see why Ken had been so against this. It would, in effect, have put them in control of their father's money. He must have felt as though they were treating him like a child who couldn't be trusted to look after his sweets properly. In actual fact that was exactly how they saw him where money was concerned, but they had to accept he would never do it.

Stephen's view now was that if any money was left for them when Ken died, then it would be an unexpected windfall. He was determined from now on not to count on any further help from his father. Stephen would use his own money to provide for his family. He would make his money work for him and provide a legacy for his own branch of the family. At least he could be certain that his children would never have to scrimp and save.

It was time to go through to the departure lounge. The flight would be leaving within the hour. Stephen felt his heart pound with a rush of adrenalin as he handed his passport over to be checked.

The girls had relaxed and seemed excited by the journey ahead. It would be a long haul, but they'd coped well the last time. They had all liked Australia and were thrilled at the prospect of living there permanently. They must also have had their fill of the tension and bickering at home. A fresh start was something they deserved more than he and Susan even.

Ken had commented on how tired the girls had looked that morning – it was about all he *had* said. It had been clear that he didn't approve of them taking the girls so far away, even though he hadn't said it.

Maybe that was the problem with the Whites. So much was left bubbling under the surface. One thing about the money was that it had brought to the surface a lot of resentment within the family. Without it those feelings might have festered for years, but they would surely have come out eventually.

He felt anger towards his father for many reasons, yet Ken probably knew nothing of how or why he felt that way. Stephen thought his dad had treated his mum terribly at times. Even though he knew she could be hard to live with, he often wondered if being with Ken all her adult life had in part made her the way she was. He guessed that his father thought it all boiled down to money – it didn't.

Stephen resented the way his dad was with Richard. Despite everything he had put the family through, and continued to put them through with this trial due to start next month, Ken was still tolerant of his youngest child's behaviour.

Maybe if he had told him some of this before he left they could have cleared the air. It was too late now.

A gust of hot air from the aircraft's massive engines crossed Stephen's face as he slowly climbed up the steps leading into the aircraft. It was a taste of the warmth that would greet them when finally they arrived at their destination.

'Wave goodbye to Manchester, kids,' he called out, gulping back an unexpected wave of emotion. The six of them stood together, holding back the queue for a few seconds as they waved towards the terminal.

Stephen took Susan's hand in his and smiled at her. Tears were streaming down her cheeks, but she smiled too.

'Here's where it all starts for us,' he said, battling against the lump in his throat. 'It's just us now, Susan – thank God!'

They stepped into the plane and Stephen took one last glance at the terminal. He hoped one day he would return and step on to the tarmac at this same airport ready to start afresh with his dad. There was surely a chance they could resolve their differences and have a relationship they could both enjoy.

Chapter Twelve

Richard spat out the dregs of vomit into the lavatory bowl and quickly flushed them away. He had been looking forward to this day for months, but now it was here he was petrified.

Today he would stand in the dock and give evidence in his defence. Richard had made a dash for the bathroom after a sickening wave of panic had overwhelmed him as he ate breakfast with the children. He hadn't even been aware that he was thinking about the trial at the time. Ben had been mithering him to take him out on his quad over at his Uncle David's farm at the weekend and Richard had agreed. The instant he said yes he remembered his barrister warning him that he could face up to years in prison if he were found guilty. Days out messing around with his children would be off the agenda. He would miss out on seeing them grow up.

The possibility that he could be found guilty had haunted Richard since his arrest. It was a fear he had kept well hidden, preferring to put on a show of bravado in front of family and friends. If they knew he was scared then they would be too.

Richard was frightened by the mere fact that he

was appearing in court in the first place. He had answered every question put to him at his arrest honestly and accurately, yet the police had still charged him with a crime he knew nothing about. Then he had spent two weeks on remand in Strangeways. If a mistake had landed him in there so easily, then another could also see him wrongly found guilty by the jury.

He and Julie had lain in bed, snuggled up together, while the kids ran riot downstairs, for as long as they could get away with that morning. Neither of them had acknowledged what was happening today. There was no point.

The children remained oblivious to the saga unfolding in the courtroom just a few miles up the road from where they went to school. Richard and Julie had even cancelled their copy of the *Manchester Evening News* for the duration of the trial in case the children picked it up and read about it.

Every morning, as Richard left for Manchester Crown Court, Ben looked him up and down, confusion written across his face. He did again that morning. 'Why are you all dressed up, Dad?' he asked. He rarely saw his father dressed like that in the daytime.

'I've got to go to a meeting, mate,' Richard told him.

'But, Daddy, you've been going to meetings for ages now. Why?'

'Oh, it's too boring to explain. Now come on, get your shoes on. You'll be late for school.'

Richard worried desperately about his children and the effect it would have on them if he was sent to prison. He imagined them being teased in the playground and felt churned up with anger at the injustice of it all.

Most of the people involved in the smuggling operation had pleaded guilty by now. But the police were still determined to see him go down with them. It was as though they had become obsessed by him. They refused to accept or even consider that he could, as he repeatedly told them, have been oblivious to what was going on behind his back.

His company had hired out a trailer that had then been used to smuggle drugs. He had known nothing about it. That was not a crime. He still couldn't understand why he was still having to fight to get that message over. He just prayed that the jury would see the charge for what it was – a sham. Richard's own theory was that he had been used as a pawn to get publicity for the operation. By throwing a big lottery winner into the frame, the police were guaranteed to get in the papers.

The press had been to his house to take photographs. He knew they wouldn't be using them if he was acquitted. There would be no story then, and that infuriated him. He had watched the reporters scribbling away in their notebooks whenever he or the lottery money was mentioned. Some of them had looked him up and down as he stood in the dock – not seeing him as a person but as someone who would provide them with a good story. They didn't care that he and his family were enduring a living hell through it all.

Richard had had to bite his tongue many times since he had been released on bail. He would be stood at the bar in his local listening to what people just yards away from him were whispering about him. They acted as if they were the judge and jury in all this, saying he was guilty as hell. If he did get off, he heard them say, it was only because of his dad's money and the legal defence team he had paid for. He felt like punching their lights out, but that wasn't an option. He was out on a million-pound bail – he'd had a taste of prison life and was desperate not to go back there.

Since his release, Richard had tried not to dwell too much on the two weeks he had spent behind bars. He had barely discussed it with anyone other than Julie and his father. There were things he found difficult to tell even them.

He had been hell to live with at times during the last few months. He was amazed how Julie had put up with his massive mood swings and explosions of temper. She must have bitten her tongue so many times as she soothed him.

Julie never pushed Richard for details – she didn't expect him to sit down and analyse what he had been through and the effect it had had on him. His dad was the same. They were there if he needed to talk, and they were there if he needed to shout. They understood the pain he was in without his having to spell out to them why. Richard was hurting for many reasons. The very fact that he was on trial for a crime he didn't commit had destroyed his confidence in the whole concept of fair play. He had since learnt that some of the people who had pleaded guilty had been on the peripheries of his new crowd of drinking friends. One in particular had helped him get in with this new crowd.

They had used him, as had the police, who, along

with Customs, had to know he was innocent. They had him guilty by association and it stank. They didn't give a toss if he went down for this – they just wanted the headlines so that their bosses would read in the papers how hard they'd been working.

David and Stephen, his own brothers, had given him little support, and he hated them for the way they were handling things. Stephen had run off to Australia to avoid any bad publicity. He made no attempt to help Richard through his ordeal – all he could think about was himself and what the neighbours might say.

David had been little better, and at times Richard had wished David had gone to Australia with Stephen. David was a wind-up merchant – he had spent months cracking jokes and teasing Julie about the possibility of Richard going back inside. He and Stephen had barely been able to contain their smugness since he came out. It was as though they viewed his two weeks on remand as appropriate punishment for his hanging out with people they didn't like. David never tired of pointing out that he had told him so all along. That was something he really didn't need right now.

He and Stephen had barely spoken in the run-up to his emigration. Stephen had left the country at loggerheads with him and their father. It was as though he thought he didn't need his family now he had his money. He wanted to go and start a new life where no one would know how he got his million. He was a snob who hated people knowing he was a lottery winner. It seemed that he thought he was better than that.

Richard still found it hard to accept Stephen's and

David's attitudes towards Ken. Since Sheila had died they had desperately tried to get their dad's money put out of his reach. They wanted to control it and give Ken pocket money. To Richard that was a disgusting way to treat the man who had given them so much. They were more concerned about keeping an eye on their inheritance and making sure Richard didn't get his hands on it than they were about their own father's feelings.

They were ruled by money and, having had a taste of it, were now focused only on getting more of it. While Richard realised he had been stupid at times, he would rather that than have turned out greedy like his brothers.

The way he saw it, whatever their dad chose to do with his money was his business – nobody else's. He had given them a million pounds each – that had been generous enough. How many fathers would have done that in the first place? Even if Ken died leaving them nothing, that was fine by Richard. His father was his father – not a bank account they could get their hands on when he died.

Richard was devastated by the way his brothers dismissed that time he spent in Strangeways as simply his getting what he deserved. They had never even tried to find out what it had really been like in there. He was still haunted by one incident when he had been placed in a holding cell while he waited to meet one of his legal team during his remand. He had been put in with several other prisoners who were all smoking. The smoke had begun to choke him, and he had asked one of the screws to leave the door open slightly so that he could have some air.

The warder had taken offence at him for daring to

ask and immediately ordered him into a side room, where he had strip-searched him. To the prison officer that had simply been a way of showing his power over Richard; to Richard it was another moment of degradation which left him feeling violated.

David knew none of this. But while he joked about the possibility of Richard returning to prison, he was turning a huge knife inside him without even realising it.

Ken had been different. He had yelled at Richard sometimes, telling him what an idiot he had been, but he had never gloated in the way his brothers had at times. Far from it – the strain of the trial and the build-up to it had taken its toll on Ken. There were times when he looked ill with worry.

Richard and Ken had always been close. They had a mutual respect and treated one another as equals. David took great delight in scolding Ken like a naughty child for the way he frittered his money.

Stephen was downright jealous of their relationship. Richard even had a sneaking suspicion that his older brother was jealous of the fact that he was the only one of them who had a son himself. Stephen and Susan had four girls and had never made a secret of the fact that they wanted a boy. When Ben had been born they had seemed envious. Things had gone from bad to worse between them since then.

Richard could not pinpoint a reason why he and Stephen had grown so far apart. He sometimes wondered if it had started as a kind of game between them that had developed into a feud since the lottery win. Stephen tensed up the moment they were in a room together these days. At times he had been

Rachel Halliwell

embarrassed to have Stephen for a brother. He was totally dominated by his wife and his money. It was pathetic.

Julie left the house with the children. She was dropping them off at her sister's house on her way to court. Ken would be calling for him in a few minutes. Julie had been amazing throughout all of this. They had been away for the weekend just before the trial had started and she hadn't once mentioned the trial. She knew instinctively that he would talk about it only when he felt he could. If she had pushed him he would have shut down on her. The kids were oblivious to what was going on, largely because she had kept her cool.

Richard stepped into the dock, his palms hot and cold at the same time. The press bench was full today – the journalists must have known he would be giving evidence. He took a deep breath and swore his oath on the Bible. This was his moment to tell that jury how it was. It was simple to him and surely would be to them too. He didn't know what was going on with his company – he had committed no crime. Richard had to trust them to see this trial for what it was – a complete and utter sham.

Richard clutched the sides of the dock as he answered the questions put to him by his defence barrister. He quickly relaxed as he found his confidence, explaining the effect that such a huge amount of money thrust on him had had on his life.

'The hardest thing was living at home,' he told the court. 'Getting used to being with her indoors. It was always playtime for me. That caused a lot of rows.'

His barrister pushed him for more details. Richard obliged, reeling off the trips he had made without his family and the days and nights spent drinking in Manchester.

As he explained the lifestyle he had grown to enjoy – admitting to the jury that he had lived like a playboy – it was clearer to him than ever before that he would be acquitted. He had been an idiot. He had trusted people he shouldn't have. He had spent his money having a great time. There was no denying any of that. But he had never touched drugs and certainly didn't peddle them. He failed to see how the prosecution could twist any of that to make him look guilty.

Now it was the turn of the prosecution. Richard braced himself for their questions. Once this was over he would have nothing left to do but to wait for the jury to decide his fate.

He was suddenly being bombarded with questions about phone calls he was supposed to have made to his co-defendants – telephone calls he knew nothing about. They were made on his mobile, but he regularly lent that mobile to other people. No – he couldn't remember exactly to whom he had lent it or when. He just knew that he didn't recognise any of the numbers they were throwing at him and that whoever had dialled them hadn't been him.

Next they wanted to know about a trip he had made to Spain. He had gone to buy pots for his father's patio. They couldn't accept that – they didn't believe that anyone would travel so far to buy pots that they could have picked up at a garden centre in this country. He felt as though he was banging his head against a brick wall. That was the way he lived then; that was the kind of thing he did to pass the time. It was just coincidence that the drugs had been imported from Spain soon after that trip. Why didn't they believe him?

Next came questions about his lack of involvement with the business. He had put people in whom he trusted – he felt let down. No – he hadn't known that his vehicles had been hired out to bring drugs into the country. He had been too busy out enjoying himself to know what was going on. He answered every question put to him – nothing had been proved against him. He just wanted to go home and get on with his life. He wanted to get back on the road and earn a living again. He wanted this to end.

Then the questions stopped. Richard could do nothing else to present his case. He had to wait for the verdict.

Chapter Thirteen

RICHARD SAT AS THOUGH IN A TRANCE as the prosecution and defence summed up the case against him. He was tired, desperate for it to end so he could start thinking about something else. The story was verging on being boring now; he'd heard it so many times. The defence said he knew nothing. The prosecution said he was the money behind the crime. They were going round in circles.

The judge began his summing-up. Richard expected him to spew out a whole load of legal jargon that would mean nothing to anyone but the barristers at the front of the court.

But what the judge was saying made sense. He was telling the jurors how Richard White had cooperated fully with the investigation, that he had answered every question put to him. He even told them that where Richard was concerned the prosecution had continually moved the goalposts – every time he convinced them he knew nothing of the conspiracy they came up with another way he could have been involved. The judge actually said that not only had they moved the goalposts but they had also moved the entire playing field.

Richard felt an instant boost to his confidence. That, to him, sounded as if the judge was on his side.

Suddenly the jury were on their feet, making their way to the private room down the hall where they would deliberate for as long as it was going to take them to decide his fate.

The sun streamed through the tall windows along the corridor outside the courtroom. The heat was stifling.

Richard loosened his tie and took off his jacket. Julie was sitting, her head in her hands, next to his father. He had never seen Ken look so tired before. His eyes darted across the corridor every time someone came from the direction of the jury room. People talked to him but his dad was only pretending to listen. He looked scared. Richard wanted this over now as quickly as possible – not just for him but for his father too.

By five o'clock there was no verdict and so the judge sent everyone home. That night Richard couldn't eat or sleep – trying to put on some show of normality for the children had been one of the hardest things he had ever done. He had been relieved when they finally went to bed and he could stop pretending that everything was all right. Even though he knew he could face up to eight years away from them after tomorrow, he needed space that evening to prepare for what lay ahead the next day. He was frightened he might break down in front of them. The last thing he wanted was to drag them into this mess when Julie had managed to keep them away from it for all these months.

* * *

The next morning Richard patted Ben on the head as he left the house. 'No more meetings after today, mate,' he told him.

Ben grinned back. 'Don't forget you're taking me out on the quad at the weekend.'

Richard nodded. 'Oh, yeah – like you'd let me forget.'

Ken arrived to drive Richard into court. 'You're all right, little'n. It'll be over this time tomorrow,' he said as he started the engine.

'Yeah,' said Richard. 'Then we can get on with suing the bastards.'

'Let's just get today over with first, eh? Then we've got all the time in the world to sort them out.'

They walked from the car-park to the Crown Court building in silence. The press photographers and TV crews were waiting to get the pictures of his arrival.

'You won't be fucking interested when I get off, will you?' he snarled quietly in their direction. 'Fucking parasites.'

'Just keep control of that temper today, Richard,' his father warned him. 'We play it by the book right to the end today and you'll have nothing to worry about. A few hours and we'll be going home. Then you can crack open a few bottles of that champagne you seem to like so much!'

Richard couldn't even bring himself to smile at his dad. His head was too full of moments flashing back into his mind from the last few months. He was thinking about his mum too. She had died never knowing if he would go to prison or be acquitted. He had so wanted her to see his name cleared. Now that could never happen and it devastated him.

David was due at the court that day, and Richard was determined he wouldn't use it as a chance to wind him, and in particular Julie, up. He didn't know if it was David's way of coping with difficult situations or if he actually enjoyed upsetting her with his stupid jokes. All Richard knew was that he was in the mood to punch him if he tried any of that today.

The day dragged on. It felt like being at school – forced to stay in a hot, sticky building while decisions were being made about him that he had no control over. The building even smelt like school, with its musty air and kids loitering in corridors.

Julie's smoking was beginning to get on his nerves.

'Can you put that out,' he snapped at her. 'Go and smoke in the canteen if you've got to.'

She sighed and stood up to leave. He grabbed her hand and squeezed it. She smiled back at him. He wasn't angry with her. She and his dad were the only people he didn't feel angry with at that moment. They had supported him without question and would stick by him whatever decision the jury made.

While the prospect of returning to prison chilled his whole being, he knew that, if he had to, he would survive it. Meanwhile, Julie and Ken would do everything they could to prove his innocence. They wouldn't let him rot away in a prison cell for a moment longer than he had to. He trusted them to look out for him, whatever happened today.

Ken had already promised him he would use every penny he had left to launch an appeal. His brothers would hate that – their inheritance being squandered to get him his freedom. He wanted their support – he felt he deserved it as their brother. But Stephen hadn't even been prepared to stay in the country while the court case took place, which Richard felt spoke volumes about what he really thought.

Richard couldn't understand what was taking so long. The jury had been out since lunchtime yesterday – more than twenty-four hours had passed since then.

One minute he thought it was a good sign – it meant the jurors were being careful, going back over all the evidence without rushing their decision; after all, his liberty was at stake here – but then he would think that they were taking their time because they were considering convicting him. They would hardly take a decision that would see a man locked up for several years without taking their time over it. If they had thought he was innocent they would have come back straight away. There would have been nothing to think about.

These thoughts continued through the afternoon. They were peppered with moments when the pressure was too much and he would explode at Julie and Ken, telling them how he shouldn't have been there in the first place. They would spend their time calming him and preparing for the next explosion.

Richard had just about reconciled himself to another sleepless night while the jury continued to deliberate when suddenly Aiden appeared at his side. He looked serious. Richard was in no doubt what he was about to say and just nodded. The jury was back in.

Julie put her arms around his neck and kissed him gently on the cheek. 'We're going home in few minutes, babe,' she whispered. 'It's nearly over.'

Tears were streaming down her cheeks as she

spoke, but she smiled through them. He wanted to cry with her, but he didn't dare to. If he started he might never stop. He wanted to take her hand and walk out of there without waiting for the verdict. It filled him with horror that he was not allowed to do that.

For a moment he felt consumed with panic. In a few minutes from now he could be led back into a holding cell with nothing to look forward to other than finding out where he was to do his time.

But he composed himself, forcing his legs to take him back into court to hear the verdict.

Richard's heart felt as though it had jumped into his throat as the foreman rose to his feet. The judge asked him if they had all come to the same conclusion. They had not. He then asked if they had come to a majority decision. They had.

'How do you find the defendant, Richard White . . . guilty or not guilty?'

Time went into slow motion as the foreman opened his mouth to speak. Richard stared at him – willing him to say the words he had waited months to hear.

'Not guilty.'

He heard Julie scream from the balcony. He strained his neck up towards the public gallery behind him to try to see her and his father.

He began to laugh – not from happiness but from incredible relief. He felt tears prick his eyes. He looked at the jurors and grinned. They had believed him, and he wanted to go over and thank them for what they had done. They had listened to him and accepted what he had told them. He had never felt more grateful in all his life.

Outside the courtroom Julie and his father were waiting. Ken had colour in his cheeks for the first time in the seven weeks the trial had taken. Julie looked radiant. It was only now that he realised her face had been covered with worry lines for weeks. He could see that because now they had gone.

The press wanted to talk to him – they could wait. He knew whatever he said was unlikely to get in the papers. They hadn't got the verdict they wanted; this was not a story for them. He just wanted to get out of that building and on with his life. He didn't want to stay there a moment longer than he had to.

But there was something Richard needed to do before he could go home and start celebrating. It was something he had to do on his own. He told Julie to go home with Ken and that he would see them back at the house in a couple of hours. They didn't question him. He guessed they knew where he was going.

Richard knelt at his mother's graveside and placed on the ground the tulips he had bought at a shop on the way to the cemetery.

'Oh, Mum,' said Richard quietly as he spread the flowers out in one of the vases his dad had left for her. 'I've got some news for you.'

He began to cry. 'They acquitted me, Mum. They believed me – the jury believed me. They found me not guilty.'

Richard's body began to shake as he allowed himself to cry like a baby. 'I'm so sorry you weren't there, Mum. I'm so sorry you didn't get to see it for yourself.'

'She did see it, son. Of course she saw it.'

Richard spun round. It was his dad.

He quickly wiped his tears from his face with the sleeve of his jacket.

'She will have watched every bit of it with us,' said Ken, his own face blotchy from his own tears of relief.

'What are you doing here, Dad?' Richard asked.

'Same as you, lad. Just letting your mum know that our little'n is all right. Come on, now. Julie's in the car and she wants to get you home.'

'Can you just give me a minute, Dad? I just want a bit longer alone with her.' Ken nodded and walked a short distance away.

'The money's nearly gone, Mum,' he said quietly, brushing some stray leaves off the headstone. 'We're not exactly skint, but I'm going to get myself back to work. I need to start grafting again – put money on the table for my family. At least I know where I'm up to then.'

He rose to his feet. 'I'm so sorry about the upset I caused, but at least you know now that it really didn't have anything to do with me. I'm glad you know.'

He nodded over to his father, who took his place at the graveside. Richard walked on ahead so that Ken could now have a moment alone with her. Each step towards the car felt lighter than normal. He stopped and looked around the beautiful cemetery his dad had chosen for Sheila. He'd never appreciated his surroundings so deeply in all his life. He thought once more of where he could have been right now had the verdict been different. Then he shook himself free of it and smiled. He had some celebrating to do.

Chapter Fourteen

KEN WALKED BACK INTO THE HOUSE and took off his coat. Suddenly he felt shattered. It had been an incredible day. That moment, as he waited for the foreman to announce his verdict, had been terrifying. He had closed his eyes and willed the words 'not guilty' to come from that man's mouth. When he said just that, Ken had felt the earth sway beneath his feet. Nothing could have stopped the guttural yelp of delight that left his mouth a split second later. He had never known relief like it. Tears had sprung from his eyes even though he had never felt less like crying. His boy was coming home with him.

Ken walked over to the telephone. He had become good friends with a woman called Audrey Long since Sheila died. She had been supportive throughout the trial, and he was keen to share their good news. She, more than most, knew the terrible strain this whole episode had been. Many nights he had confided in her during their telephone conversations or days out together. Only she truly knew how terrified he had been that his youngest son could end up in prison for a crime Ken knew he didn't commit.

Audrey was thrilled to hear the outcome and

promised to catch a train up to Cheshire from her home in North Wales the next day. Ken booked a table at their favourite restaurant for dinner and then went upstairs to get ready for the party.

The victory party was held at the Comfortable Gill, Richard's local. All his pals were there, along with friends of the family and people who worked for him and David. Spirits were high, and with a free bar courtesy of Ken the night looked set to be a long one.

Ken wished Stephen could have been there, but he was settling down to his new life in Australia. Ken had phoned him to tell him that his brother had been acquitted, but Stephen had sounded unimpressed. Ken hoped it was just an act and that he was really as delighted as they all were. In time, now the trial was behind them, he was sure they would heal the rift between them.

Ken looked around at the people in the bar. It reminded him of the night he held the party to celebrate his win. Only that night the atmosphere had been one of excitement while tonight it was one of great relief.

He couldn't help but think that the two events they had marked in this way were linked. It was hard to believe that Richard would ever have appeared in that courtroom if he hadn't had the lottery money to distract him from his work. If he had been out on his lorry, instead of living it up in Manchester, Richard would never have met the people who got him into this trouble.

He glanced over at his son. Richard was surrounded by his pals, knocking back champagne straight from the bottle. He was having a great time.

Tonight, thought Ken, would need to be the last he spent living it up for a while. It was time for Richard to get back to work and back on track. Not that he had too much choice in it. The high spending was catching up with him and Julie, and their funds were running out. Ken was certain that was for the best. Richard would be better without the burden of so much money.

They left the pub in the early hours. Ken lay in bed thinking of the future. He hadn't dared before now. In the back of his mind he had always had a fear that Richard could go to prison. Then he would have had to devote every penny and every waking moment to getting him freed.

His other sons would have been against him – they had already made it very clear that they wouldn't have wanted him to fund an appeal. But he wouldn't have cared about that. He would have done the same for any of his children. The other two thought he was soft on Richard, that he was his favourite. It amazed him that they could think like that when they had children of their own. They should know that you just don't have favourites. He would take Audrey away for a holiday – they could talk about it tomorrow. Ken fell asleep, more easily than he had thought possible in the last few months.

Ken and Audrey first met back in the 1950s when she was a telephonist for the General Post Office with his sister Mavis. Ken had just come out of the army and took little notice of his sister's teenage friends unless they were male and he had to vet them for their mother. Audrey was an attractive girl but incredibly shy in Ken's company. Ken was too busy chasing after Sheila to consider the then seventeen-year-old Audrey as a possible partner.

When Ken and Sheila moved to the north-west in the 1970s Audrey was an occasional visitor. She and Mavis had remained firm friends throughout their lives and would come to stay at the house with their husbands on their way to Blackpool each year to see the illuminations. Ken and Sheila would spend a night at the resort with them before leaving them to enjoy their holiday.

When Mavis emigrated to New Zealand the link was gone. The only contact they had with Audrey after that was when his sister came back to England to visit her family and friends and then to appear on the lottery show.

The next time Ken saw Audrey was at Sheila's funeral, when she joined Mavis to pay her respects. Ken had barely noticed her there as he grieved for his dead wife.

Six weeks later Mavis had asked Ken to join her at the house in Newport where she was staying before returning to New Zealand. She suggested they spend some time with Audrey, who was going through a difficult time herself. Audrey had been separated from her husband for several years after a difficult marriage and had struggled alone raising their three children. Mavis had been upset to see Audrey so withdrawn, her only interest outside her children being her job on the switchboard at the local hospital, where she worked night and day.

Ken couldn't face visiting the house that was so much a part of Sheila, so he suggested that Mavis should bring her husband and Audrey to stay with him in Cheshire instead. They spent the weekend eating out in restaurants and relaxing at the house. Ken enjoyed their company and felt comfortable with Audrey, talking about the old times when they had all lived in Newport as youngsters.

Ken had felt sorry to see them leave on the Monday morning. Audrey had to get back to do her shift at the hospital that evening. Ken took them all to the railway station, and as their train pulled in he put his arms around Audrey in a farewell embrace. Physical contact like that was normally alien to Ken, but for Mavis it was a way of life. It felt natural in her company to do it. For a moment Ken felt embarrassed by his show of affection towards a woman who had been an acquaintance for years yet he didn't know particularly well. Audrey's smile as he pulled away from her put him at his ease.

Later that week Ken was opening his mail. The begging letters had eased off a few months after the win but, since news of Sheila's death had been reported in the newspapers, they were coming in again almost daily. In among the regular post he noticed that three letters were handwritten. He sighed as he opened the first, hoping it would be one offering condolences and not a veiled request for money. Since the win he'd had letters from people wanting him to help them set up new businesses, pay off their mortgage arrears, and even one from a woman who wanted him to pay for her breasts to be enlarged.

This letter started off well with the writer saying how sorry she was to hear about Sheila's death. Her own husband had died two years earlier, and she said she could empathise with Ken and what he was going through. Then it went on to say how she was struggling to make ends meet now she was alone and could Ken find it in his heart to help her. He stopped reading then and picked up the second letter. He tore open the envelope and pulled out the sheets of pink notepaper inside. A Polaroid photograph felt out from between the pages. It was of a young woman stark naked posing provocatively. Ken threw it into the wastepaper basket beside him, along with the letter which he didn't bother to read. At one time he might have taken a peek at the picture just for his own amusement; today he didn't even find it funny. He just felt annoyed that someone could have so little respect for grief.

He noticed that the third letter had been posted in Newport the day before. He pulled a card out from the envelope. Ken felt confused when he saw the words 'thank you' printed across the front above a vase of roses. He couldn't remember the last time someone had sent him a thank-you card and quickly checked the envelope to see if it really was for him.

A smile spread across Ken's face as he read it. He had already looked to the end and knew now that it was from Audrey. It began by thanking him for a wonderful weekend during which she felt she had left reality behind for a few days. It said what a kind and generous man she thought he was and told him how enjoyable it had been for her to spend time in his world – it had made returning to her own small house and her job at the hospital more bearable.

Ken felt deeply moved by the letter and, as he placed it on the coffee table, he reached for the telephone to call Audrey. Her son Ian answered and explained that she was away for a couple of weeks visiting her daughter Michelle in America.

Ken remembered that Audrey had mentioned the trip during her stay. That was one of the reasons she worked so many hours at the hospital – so that she could fly out to the States twice a year. His sister had told him how she would work double shifts several times a week when her children were at college to pay for their fees. She still did it, even working on Christmas Day if she was asked to, determined not to let the hospital down. At that time Audrey's life revolved around the hospital and, being a staunch Catholic, going to church.

When she got back from America Audrey returned Ken's call. He invited her to visit again – this time without Mavis, who had gone back to New Zealand. They arranged that she would come in the January.

There was a little awkwardness between them when he collected Audrey from the station when she arrived. They had never spent any time alone before; the relationship had always been dependent on his sister being around. But that soon eased as they chatted about old times again. They quickly discovered that they felt incredibly comfortable in each other's company. They were both used to spending much time alone.

Ken also realised that he found Audrey very attractive. She had always been a good-looking woman and the years had been kind to her. Even now, as she approached sixty, she looked fabulous.

After Audrey went home, Ken found himself thinking about her during every quiet moment. He wondered how she was getting on at work and at home and whether she was thinking about him. He found himself looking for her handwriting on the envelopes the postman pushed through his letter box and hoping it was her on the phone whenever it rang. He was thrilled when, two days later, he received another thank-you letter from her. For weeks they kept in touch on the telephone. Ken even put pen to paper himself and sent her a note to say that he hoped she was keeping well. He felt like a teenager again in the earliest throes of a new romance. Yet he didn't know if any romance was even likely to develop.

Finally he plucked up the courage to invite her away for a weekend. He wanted to find out if she was as interested in him as he was in her. She accepted his offer to spend a couple of days in a hotel in Dartmouth together.

When they arrived at the pretty country hotel they each went to their rooms to unpack and freshen up before dinner. Ken enjoyed getting ready to meet her in the restaurant. He had always taken great pride in his appearance. Ken never left the house without checking he looked clean and smart with a few dabs of aftershave behind each ear. He did it for himself – but tonight he was doing it for someone else. It was exciting.

They ate slowly, each so enjoying having someone to talk to they barely noticed what was on their plates. After dinner they went into the lounge, where they sat drinking coffee and brandy into the early hours. As the carriage clock on the mantelpiece chimed to tell them it was 2 a.m. Audrey made ready to go to her room.

'Before you go up, Audrey, there's something I want to ask you,' he said, staring hard into his brandy glass.

'Go on, Ken, fire away,' she replied.

'I hope you don't think I'm being presumptuous. It's just, well . . . I'm very fond of you, Audrey.'

'Oh, Ken,' she laughed. 'I've had a crush on you since I was seventeen years old!'

Ken laughed with her. 'Well, why the hell didn't you tell me then?'

'Because you were chasing after Sheila in those days. In fact, you were engaged to be married.' Then she began to look more serious. 'I wanted to tell you but I couldn't. It wouldn't have been right.'

Ken nodded in agreement. 'Aye, I suppose not.' Then he laughed again to try to ease the tension that had suddenly descended on them. 'I wish you had, though. Things might have turned out very different.'

Ken took another sip of his brandy. 'I'd like to see if we can take this friendship anywhere. What do you think?'

Audrey nodded. 'That would be nice but –'

'Ah, the dreaded but!'

'I'm still married, Ken.'

For a moment they were silent. Ken knew that Audrey's religion was the focal point in her life.

'The thing is, Audrey, if we are to be companions now and spend time together and go away together, I can't accept that it will always be a platonic relationship. I want more than that. I want us to have a complete friendship.'

There was silence again before Audrey spoke. 'I understand that, Ken, but you have to accept that while I'm married there can never be anything like that for us. It goes against everything I believe in.'

They left the conversation there, but Ken dwelt on what she had said when he went to bed. He realised

that he had grown incredibly close to Audrey in a
short time and didn't want to do anything that might
jeopardise their continuing the friendship. He
respected Audrey's devotion to her God and knew
that if she felt she had betrayed Him she wouldn't be
able to remain friends with Ken.

He also knew that Audrey's husband was keen for
a divorce and that within the next year enough time
would have passed for him to push one through even
though she had refused him one. He was a patient
man – and Audrey was worth waiting for.

Ken stood on the platform as Audrey's train pulled
in. His head was throbbing from the excesses of the
night before. He still couldn't believe that the ordeal
of the trial was over. He would take Audrey
somewhere nice for lunch to celebrate.

Audrey flung her arms around him and kissed him
warmly on the cheek. 'Oh, Ken, it's marvellous news.
You must be so happy.'

'Come on, then,' he said. 'Let's put your bags in
the car and we'll go somewhere nice for lunch.'

'Great,' beamed Audrey. 'But it's my treat, and I'm
choosing where we go.'

Audrey directed him to Harry Ramsden's, the
famous fish-and-chip diner near the motorway that
would take them home.

'I was thinking of something a bit more up-market
than this,' Ken sniffed as they got out of the car.
They went inside and he told Audrey to find a seat
while he ordered. The dining area was busy – a
coachload of pensioners had just arrived, and he
didn't want to have to wait while the waitresses took
their orders.

'They'll take our order at the table,' said Audrey. 'Now come and sit down and we can wait our turn.'

She picked up a menu and offered another to Ken. 'Look,' she said, pointing to where it said they had a special deal for senior citizens. 'We can have that.'

Ken snorted with disgust. 'Get lost,' he said. 'I'm not having that.'

'You are actually,' said Audrey. 'I'm paying and you'll have what I get for you.'

The waitress came over to take their order. Ken opened his mouth to speak but Audrey got in first.

'We'll have two senior citizen specials, please,' she said, smiling triumphantly at Ken.

After the waitress had gone Ken grabbed Audrey's hand across the wooden table. 'You could have had lunch in the poshest restaurant in Manchester – and where do we end up? Bloody Harry Ramsden's!'

They both laughed.

'It is nice eating out in fancy restaurants,' she said. 'But don't you get sick of it sometimes? It's no fun if you do it all the time. It stops being a treat.'

Ken hadn't thought of it like that before, but she did have a point. Since he didn't have to worry about how much anything cost, he had started taking things like meals out for granted. They weren't that much fun any more.

After they'd finished their meal Ken reached into his pocket for his wallet.

Audrey gently slapped him across the wrist. 'I told you – I'm paying.'

'Get away with you, woman,' said Ken, pulling a crisp ten-pound note from his wallet.

'No, Ken,' said Audrey, more firmly now. 'I said I was paying so will you just leave it at that?'

She took out the money to pay from her purse and then snapped it shut. She looked upset. Later, in the car, Audrey was quiet when normally she would have been keen to chat. Ken asked her what was wrong.

She sighed heavily. 'I just wish you didn't try to take over so much. I'm used to looking after myself and paying my own way. You have to accept that about me, Ken.'

After Audrey had gone home a couple of days later, Ken thought back to what she had said. She was right – he did tend to take over situations, especially when there was a bill to be paid. It hadn't even occurred to him until now that that might annoy someone like Audrey. She had also recently pointed out how the people around him seemed to expect him to pay for everything when they were in his company. Audrey didn't think that was right.

Maybe she had a point. They had been out recently for the day in Southport with some friends and, as usual, he had paid for everything. Afterwards Audrey had commented on the fact that they hadn't coughed up for so much as an ice cream. She had thought that was wrong, but Ken wondered what he could do to change it now.

Since they had become companions Audrey had remained very aware of what people might think her motives were for hooking up with Ken. She was frightened that some might think she was a gold-digger, only out for what she could get from him.

That couldn't have been further from the truth – Ken had no doubts about that. She insisted on paying her own way when they were out together and at first had been reluctant to even accept gifts from him. She worked long, hard hours and so had money of her own.

At first Stephen and David in particular had been concerned about Ken's relationship with Audrey. David worried that his father hadn't given himself enough time to grieve after losing Sheila and was looking for a replacement for his mother in Audrey. Stephen had similar concerns. But now, as they had got to know her, they seemed to understand that they were good friends and made each other happy. Ken hoped he had reassured them that she wasn't about to take Sheila's place.

In time, though, Ken dearly hoped that they would become more than companions. But while she remained married to Don he had to accept that could not happen.

Then, in August 1998, Audrey's husband died after a long illness. She and Ken had been due to go on holiday together to Germany, but Audrey was unsure now about whether she should go.

Even though they had been separated for almost five years she still felt duty-bound to see to the arrangements after his death. She had helped care for him right up until he died, never forgetting the vows she'd made when she'd married him. Eventually she decided to go ahead with the trip after the hospital where he died told her there could be no funeral until a full autopsy had taken place. There was nothing she could do for Don for at least three weeks.

Audrey remained subdued throughout the holiday. Ken guessed that she was grieving not only for the man that had died but also for the marriage that had gone so wrong for her. He had got to know Audrey's three children, Justine, Michelle and Ian, quite well by now, and they often commented on how happy their mother had been since they had become friends.

Audrey had been devastated when the marriage had broken down. She had worked hard to save it, but it had been hopeless. In the end she had had to accept that she was better off without him. Since her children had grown up she spent much of her time alone and saw little of other people. They told Ken that they had never heard her laugh so much. It made him feel good.

At the end of the holiday Ken decided to go and pack Audrey's suitcase for her. He had already put his own belongings away ready for the journey home and wanted to get hers ready for the porter to take down.

Audrey walked into her hotel bedroom as he was laying her clothes out on the bed. He had always done the packing for both himself and Sheila when she was alive. His first job when they arrived at their destination would be to unpack everything and put it all away while Sheila got herself a cup of tea and a fag. It was something he took great pride in doing well. Even Sheila had failed to fault him at it.

He beamed at Audrey, waiting for her to compliment him on what a good job he was doing. She just stood and stared at him.

'It's all right, love. You go down to reception and get yourself a nice cup of tea, and I'll get this lot packed for you.' He tipped the contents of a drawer on to the bed and began to sort through the array of scarves and handkerchiefs.

'I'll do no such thing,' said Audrey angrily. 'What the hell do you think you're playing at, Ken White? What are you doing with my things?'

'I'm packing for you,' said Ken, startled by her tone.

'Well, I can do my own packing, thank you. Now, you go downstairs and get a drink and leave me to sort my own things out.'

Ken didn't know what to say. He had no idea what he had done to upset her so much. 'I'm just –'

'Just nothing. Get out of my room, Ken, and wait for me downstairs.'

'Oh, blow you,' Ken snapped. 'Do your own bloody packing, then.' He slammed the door behind him as he left, muffling the sound of Audrey's furious response.

When the car arrived to take them to the airport Ken hoped Audrey would be in a better mood. She tutted as he held the door open for her.

'What was all that about, then?' he asked as the car pulled away.

'I'm Audrey, not Sheila,' she said quietly.

'What the hell is that supposed to mean?'

'It means you can stop running around after me the way you did with her. I don't need it, Ken, and I certainly don't want it. Why do you always have to be in control – always running the show? It's not for me.'

Ken didn't answer her. But later, when they got back home, he thought about her comments. On reflection he had to accept that there was truth in what she had said. He did like to be in control and had been very dominant in his relationship with Sheila. It was something he had always thought

Sheila had wanted. He had never had cause to doubt it.

Perhaps if he had behaved differently their marriage could have been better. It was too late now – Sheila was gone and there was no bringing her back. But he did have another chance at happiness with Audrey. Now that they were moving on from being companions to lovers he realised he had to change. With her help he was confident he could do it.

Two months after the Germany trip Ken took Audrey on a Mediterranean cruise. They were now accepted as a couple by everyone they knew. Despite that, Audrey still insisted on having her own bedroom at the house. Until recently she had stayed in one of the spare bedrooms whenever she was there. Ken had finally persuaded her to let him have it decorated in her own style so that it would always be hers. When they were apart he often went into the room, which was now a mass of pink and frills. He enjoyed sitting on the bed thinking of the next time they would be together. When she was at the house he would creep across the landing after they had gone to bed hoping for a cuddle at least. It made him feel young again.

Ken beamed with pride when Audrey joined him at their table for dinner on the first night of the cruise. She looked beautiful in her long blue evening dress, its plunging neckline and nipped-in waist showing off her figure. She had just turned sixty yet had the looks of a woman twenty years her junior. He noticed she was wearing the gold watch he had bought her on their trip to Germany.

After dinner the band started to play. He stood up and

offered her his arm. She smiled as she linked her own in his. They danced all evening, spinning around the dance floor to whatever the band played. He had never met a woman who loved to dance as much as she did. He had never felt so proud to be seen with someone as he did that night. He thought he might be falling in love.

That cruise seemed to cement their relationship. The following year they would travel the world together on a two-month cruise. When Audrey retired from her job at the hospital, she and Ken spent most of their time together, either in Cheshire or North Wales. They hated being apart.

Audrey made no secret of the fact that she thought that Ken was parted from his money too easily. He was asked regularly to make donations to charities and causes he had no link with, and often he made contributions because he felt guilty if he didn't.

A few days before their first Christmas as a couple, Ken took a phone call from his wine merchant, who was based in Merseyside. He had seen a poster in his local church asking parishioners to help raise three thousand pounds for a lad with cerebral palsy. He thought Ken might like to donate the full amount himself to send the boy away on a trip.

Ken told the man he would think about it but pointed out that the boy, whom he had never met, wasn't even local to him.

'You're thinking you should send that money anyway, aren't you?' said Audrey as he put the telephone down.

'Aye, I was,' he agreed, rubbing his forehead as if deep in thought.

'Ken, stop it. You don't have to feel guilty about

having this money, you know. You don't have to keep trying to please everyone who comes your way. That man had no right to ask you to make a donation. He abused his knowledge of you through his job to try to help someone you don't even know. Send him a few quid if you must – but don't beat yourself up for not sending three thousand pounds. It's time you got used to having this money and stopped handing it out like sweets. It's got to last you a few years yet.'

Later that afternoon Ken walked into the lounge where Audrey was just finishing a conversation on the telephone with her son Ian.

'All right, love. I'll speak to you soon,' he heard her say. 'Bye now – I love you too.'

Ken sat down and picked up his newspaper. He put it down again without even looking at it.

'Is everything all right, Ken?' she asked him.

'Oh, yes. I was just thinking.'

'What about?'

'Oh, I was just wondering if there's maybe something missing in me. Listening to you on the phone then. The way you and your family tell each other you love each other all the time.'

Audrey laughed. 'What's wrong with that, then?'

'Nothing. Nothing at all wrong with that,' said Ken. 'It's just something I've never done with my family. It makes me wonder if all my life I've maybe fought the system. I just feel that I've maybe never had the time to think much about love or find out what it really means.'

Ken reflected on his life, grasping for the times he had told his wife or his children that he loved them. Somehow the words just got stuck in his throat.

He had presumed they knew without him having to say it. He and Sheila had told each other that they loved each other in their early days together, but that habit had been lost over the years.

Yet it seemed as if Audrey and her family used the word 'love' every time they were together. It came naturally to all of them.

He wondered if he was that way because of his upbringing. But then he had to admit that his sister Mavis was an extremely affectionate woman who felt no awkwardness with using the word either. They had grown up together yet when it came to expressing love they were so different. He remembered times when Sheila was alive and they had visited Mavis in New Zealand. He and his wife would exchange glances of surprise and confusion even as Mavis and her friends and relations would shower affection on each other without caring who was watching. It had seemed so alien to the two of them. They had mocked what they witnessed.

Yet here was Audrey, so at ease with her children. Her son and daughters clearly had no doubts about how their mother felt towards them and vice versa. Could he be so certain that his children also knew how much he loved them?

'Of course you know what love means, Ken. You love your family – and you say that you love me now.'

'Of course I love my family. We all love each other,' he said. 'It's just that it's not a word that gets bandied around very much. All I'm saying is that I thought that was normal. Now I'm not so sure. I'm beginning to wonder if I've let my boys down somehow by not telling them how I feel about them the way you do with your children.'

Rachel Halliwell

'Oh, Ken,' said Audrey, perching herself on his chair arm and taking hold of his hand. 'Love is something you just do – you don't have to worry if you're doing it right or wrong.'

Ken was still miserable. 'I've always been a good provider for my family,' he went on. 'I've always made sure they had the things that they needed, and I've never let any of them want for anything. If I've needed money for them I've soon gone out and got it – however hard I've had to work for it. To me that always meant that I was a good father.

'But then the word "love" comes an awfully hard thing for me to say sometimes, and I just don't know why. You know, I've buried my mother, my father, my brothers – I always managed to control my emotions. The only funeral I've ever cried at was Sheila's.'

He looked at Audrey and took a deep breath. 'I thought that was a good thing – I thought that meant I was a strong man. Now I think to myself: My God, Ken White – are you really the nice man you think you are? Is it really so good to be strong? Maybe I have to accept that I'm not strong, I'm just hard. I think maybe there's more to being a good father than putting money on the table. I think maybe the most important thing is to make your children feel loved, and for the first time in my life I can't be sure I've always done that.'

Audrey held her arms tightly around Ken's neck and gently kissed him on top of his head. 'Ken – don't do this to yourself. You're a lovely man and you make me feel loved. I'm sure your children feel the same.'

'Oh, Audrey. I've just started to wonder if I've

brought them up to know what's important – if I even know what's important. Look at my family. All this money we've got now and we're falling out over it.

'David and Stephen are so worried about what I'm doing with their inheritance they seem to have lost sight of what's really important. Surely it shouldn't matter to them what I leave them?

'It's my own fault – I brought them up this way and now I'm paying for it. I accuse them of being greedy but they learnt off me. I'm to blame.'

Ken smiled at Audrey. 'You're changing me, you know. You're making me look at life very differently these days.'

'Is that good?'

'Oh, yes,' said Ken. 'That's very good.'

Chapter Fifteen

USED TO PLAY THE NATIONAL LOTTERY. When it was first
launched I would buy my ticket each week and
fantasise about how I would spend my millions. But,
unlike Ken White, who was always convinced the
jackpot would be his, I never really thought I would
win. It was just a pleasant daydream. As the nation's
obsession waned, so did mine – but I would still buy
a ticket sporadically.

Now, after spending a year with a family of lottery
winners, I have stopped playing altogether – not
because I have tired of losing, but because I might
just win.

I have come to the conclusion that the burden of
overnight wealth, no matter how attractive in theory,
is in reality one I would not want to bear. The
National Lottery is gambling in its most acceptable
form. But I believe that the stakes are far higher than
the one pound it costs to buy your minimum ticket.

The biggest risk is that you will win an amount
that will change your life beyond providing basic
financial security. Two hundred thousand pounds –
enough to pay off most mortgages and put a couple
of decent cars on the drive, with money in the bank

to fall back on – would be great. It would not necessarily change your life, except for taking the edge off the kind of money worries most of us encounter from time to time. But you can't set a maximum on how much you personally would feel comfortable winning and play to that limit. It's a lottery and that's the point – you pay your pound and take your chance. If your numbers do come up, you stand to win millions. To receive that kind of money overnight, with no time to prepare for it – how could your life ever stay the same?

The majority of us are motivated to work hard for the financial rewards that it brings. We gain a sense of satisfaction in surviving until pay day or the day we receive payment for a job well done. Every pay day is a financial pat on the back and, as long as we are relatively happy with the size of that pat, it makes us feel as if we are worth something.

However distasteful the notion, we live in a society where success is judged not by how happy we are but by our standards of living and material possessions. But it's not even that simple. In all our various social brackets, we tend to judge our peers on how they got the money that gives them the same social standing as ourselves. We don't like to see someone else get it easy while we had to slog our guts out. In the eighties the old money sneered at the new – in the nineties we get to do the same with lottery winners.

The White family, like them or not, never shied from hard work. Ken's father, Richard, instilled in him as a child a work ethic that never left him. When he won the lottery, aged 64, the nation's tabloid readers rejoiced on his behalf. He was of retirement age, so was justified in putting his feet up after a lifetime's hard work. What's more, he was giving half of it away to his children. He came from a working-class town and planned to stay in the same two-up-two-down terrace he already lived in. Camelot must have been thrilled to parade him before the TV crews and newspaper reporters. Ken White was a jolly and clearly generous granddad who liked having his picture taken. He thrived on his week of fame and manipulated the media in his own canny way. Ken always knew what would make a good story – he was a tabloid reader himself and knew what lines to give the media. He told them about the time that he went bankrupt, rather than let them discover it for themselves. He stayed in control and enjoyed being famous.

But when interest in the Whites died down on a national level, Ken and his sons had to get on with being ordinary people again – set apart only by the extraordinary bank balances they now possessed. It was never going to be easy, but it proved to be harder than they could ever have anticipated. Before sending Ken away with his money, Camelot warned him that while he would remain the same person other people would change in their attitudes towards him. They explained that they would be available for advice and support for the next five years. After that he would be on his own. But in effect Ken was left to his own devices from that day, as are all the big winners in the National Lottery. With at least one new millionaire being made almost every week, it would be too much to expect any organisation to be able to keep track of them all, let alone hold their hands for five years. Of all the winners, Ken White was probably one of the best able to look after himself. He had run his own haulage business for years and was used to handling large sums of money, although admittedly not as his own personal wealth. Also, his age, and the wisdom that that tends to bring, helped him stay in control. Ken remains fond of telling how he rules his money – his money will never rule him.

Ken had nothing to prove and no axe to grind. He had salved his conscience by giving more than half of the money away and wanted to use the rest by enjoying the kind of retirement most of us can only imagine. For Ken, the very fact that he remained the same person was the hardest part of all. For a while he felt invincible and thoroughly enjoyed the money for the pleasure it could give him. It was only Richard's arrest, quickly followed by the death of his wife, that showed Ken what little value it really had. How could Camelot even begin to help him come to terms with two personal disasters as catastrophic as those?

Bitter wrangling over the money he kept for himself blew his family, fractured long before the win, apart. After setting up each of his children, for what should have been the rest of their lives, he never expected any of them to question how he spent the rest. But they did. They saw Ken's win as a legacy for future generations of the Whites, as did he in the early days. But the more pressure he felt under to invest it not for him, but for his children and grandchildren, the tighter the hold he wanted to keep over it. He felt as though he was being treated like the baby-sitter of his millions until he died. Understandably, that caused resentment all round.

What he viewed as David and Stephen's greed

made him question his own act of generosity in giving them such a large share of his winnings in the first place. With hindsight, he now wonders if he should have given them it in instalments so that they could have grown with the money. But there was no way he could ever have known how things would turn out and he took great pleasure from the gifts he made to his children.

Ken must have known how Richard would use his money. He was always the kind of person who lived for the moment: a million pounds was never going to sit in his bank account for long. Ken enjoyed watching Richard and Julie taking pleasure from the money. He was never going to judge them for what they did with it.

But he did grow concerned by Richard's change in lifestyle, away from his family. He had to acknowledge that Richard ended up before a judge and jury for a crime he could never have been accused of had he continued to work for his living.

Becoming public property was something Ken both enjoyed and resented. Outsiders suddenly felt entitled to comment on the way he lived his life – they still do. He often stands at the bar in his local listening to other drinkers discussing how, with his money, they would be off on world adventures instead of drinking bitter in the pub nearest to home. He used to bite his tongue as he stopped himself from telling them he had just returned from a world cruise. Now he just switches off because, of all his family, he is probably the most comfortable with being rich.

Ken has changed – because he had to. He has stopped caring what other people think of him and started to treat strangers with suspicion. If people discuss their own financial situation with him he is instantly on his guard, wondering if they want him to hand over some of his money to help them. It is a side to himself he does not like, but something he feels he must almost nurture to stop people taking advantage of him.

Richard, who has spent most of his share of the lottery money, is now back on the road providing for his family again. His public act of bravado throughout the trial was just that – an act. He remains deeply scarred by the time he spent in prison. The threat of returning for a hefty sentence – always a possibility – still haunts him. However stupid he might have been, he has paid the price.

These days, Richard openly admits that his dad gave him more money than he could handle. He wishes it had been less so that he would have had to keep working. Then he would never have got used to the lifestyle that landed him in so much trouble.

That said, Richard thoroughly enjoyed every minute of his spending spree. Of all the Whites, Richard got the biggest kick out of being a millionaire, even though his time being one was short lived. However boring he might think his brothers' approach to their money, their shares are still intact. Richard's mistake was one that his father did not make. Ken never tried to mix with new people and didn't see his wealth as being a passport into a new social circle. Ken's attitude was, and still is, that the money would provide comfort, not class.

Ken is happy with Audrey – the woman who has, for the first time in his life, forced him to look at himself and his behaviour. Ken knows that he must accept at least some responsibility for the way his family has turned out. As this book went to press, Ken was on the last leg of a round-the-world cruise with Audrey. While they have no plans to marry as yet, Ken is confident that they will be spending their lives together. Ironically, his children comment on how like Sheila she is.

Ken still makes regular visits to his wife's grave and is adamant that he will join her there when he dies. Their marriage might appear, on the surface, to have been a sham, but there was love between them throughout – they just weren't very good at showing it.

Meanwhile, Stephen has started a new life for himself in Australia, where he hopes no one will ever need to know how he got his wealth. He and Ken parted badly but have recently gone some way towards reconciliation after meeting up in New Zealand during Ken's travels. They have started to talk about their grievances in the hope that one day they can be resolved. When David's father handed him a million pounds, his goal in life – to provide long-term financial security for himself and his family – was suddenly achieved without any effort. That is something he is struggling to come to terms with. He enjoyed the cut and thrust of fighting to survive and having a long-term goal to work towards.

David has been forced to pull down almost a third of the house he built when he first won the money. He breached planning regulations and in the end had to bow to the local authority. It cost him more than £20,000 to do the work they deemed necessary. He remains incensed by the fact that the officers who insisted he pull the top floor down have never made an official inspection since he did it.

David seems to move quickly from one venture to another. After he finished his house, he went into business making conservatories. That company has since gone into voluntary liquidation and he has made the staff redundant. The company closed owing money locally, but from a legal point of view David is under no obligation to pay off those debts.

This has provided a new twist in the disputes between the brothers. Richard is furious that David has not personally settled his bills, while David stands his ground. From day one he was adamant that the fact that he won his money would not colour his judgment as a businessman. He was determined he would not be held personally liable for any costs incurred by his businesses.

David's latest project is as manager of a new all-girl band who are due in the studio to record their first single as this book goes to print. He is convinced they will be as successful as the Spice Girls.

These days, David rarely discusses the lottery win that made him so wealthy. He often actually denies he is a member of the same White family that hit the headlines when Ken won. He says it is to protect him from a prejudice he believes all big lottery winners meet with.

Like Stephen, he resents the way the lottery-playing public seems to see winners as having taken *their* money. He wants to be accepted as David White and not David White the lottery winner. He is concerned that he will not be taken seriously within the business community if they know his background.

It is hard, having read this book, not to question Ken White's motives in having it written. The title tells a story in itself. I also believe that what is written in it has exacerbated the problems the lottery win had already brought the Whites. They have each made discoveries they find uncomfortable. Ken's children learnt that he had been unfaithful to their mother throughout their marriage when they read the first chapter.

Discovering that Stephen had refused to stand him bail has deepened an already bitter rift between Richard and him. Richard was also deeply hurt to discover how reluctant David had been to put up any money. At one point last year, Stephen and Ken appeared on course for reconciliation. That was set back again when Stephen read how greedy his father thought he had become. That is something they continue to battle out.

I have been surprised by how candid they have all been. From day one the ground rules were clear. No one would want to read a book about a family who won the lottery and lived happily ever after. Therefore they all had to be honest about the reality of living after such a life-changing experience. They had to tell their story, warts and all.

But I could never have known just what a minefield I was walking into when I agreed to write this book. Their honesty about their relationships past and present was painful to hear, let alone tell. There are revelations they each made in separate interviews that would have had a catastrophic affect on the family if put to the rest of them. Some of the truths they did share hurt them all.

This book is a gross intrusion into the lives of four people who have no obvious reason for wanting it. Yet they are the very people who instigated it by employing someone to make it happen.

Stephen and Richard now wish they had never embarked on this project and would have preferred it if the book were not to be published. Whatever they have learnt from reading it, they would rather it had remained for the family's private consumption.

Stephen and David have both said that Ken's account of his relationship with their mother has answered many of the questions hanging over their childhoods. It made them feel closer to him and Sheila, although they wished it had been done while she was alive so that she could have given her own version. That could never have happened. While she was alive she blocked any suggestion of Ken having a book written.

When the Whites read the chapter covering Sheila's death, they were moved to tears as they remembered a unifying moment of grief. Above all, they say, the book has helped them to express the underlying resentments they felt within a family still uncomfortable with displays of emotion. They gave a stranger the information to pass between them.

It was a role that was difficult to make work and provoked conflicting feelings: on the one hand they were providing great material for the book; on the other I was being accused of stirring up trouble as I passed the details between them. That is an accusation I would not refute. But it had to be done to make this a book worth reading – exactly what they expected me to provide.

David was more realistic. He knew what he was in for from day one and so told me only what he was happy to see in print. A populist consumer himself, he knew his family's story would sell.

In the end, it was Ken's determination to see this

book published that allowed it to happen. He could have easily afforded to keep it private. I would like to think that he realised it provided a useful insight into a phenomenon of the 1990s. Or maybe he just saw a chance of some more fame.

But, whatever his motivation, it doesn't really matter. Because, no matter how scandalous the behaviour of the real-life characters in this book, a key influence over them all was the instant wealth the National Lottery gave them. That same influence is being exerted over families nationwide, and across the world wherever the lottery is played.

The Whites' lottery story is one of many. They were simply the first to tell it.